A GENTEEL ❧SPY❧

A Genteel Spy

Copyright © 2010 by Judith Riker Damon
ISBN-10:   0-9840773-8-3
ISBN-13:   978-0-9840773-8-0
Library of Congress Control Number: 2010940524

Art Direction, Cover Design and Typesetting
Copyright © 2010 by Two Peas Publishing

Photos and Illustrations
Copyright © 2010 by Judith Riker Damon

Published by:
Two Peas Publishing
PO Box 302
Rockvale, TN U.S.A.

A GENTEEL ❦SPY❦

THE INSPIRING ODYSSEY

of

Martha Broyles Royce
and her family
DURING THE CIVIL WAR

edited and illustrated by Judith Riker Damon

Two Peas Publishing
Columbia, Tennessee

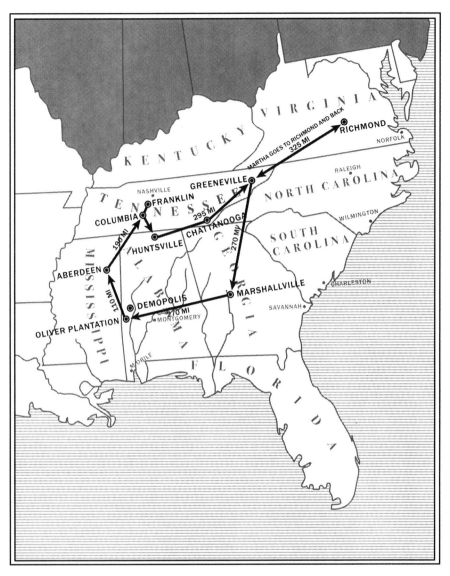

Confederate
❧ Territory ❧

THE ROYCE FAMILY TRAVELED MORE THAN 1,200 MILES,
PLUS MARTHA'S 650-MILE TRIP TO RICHMOND.

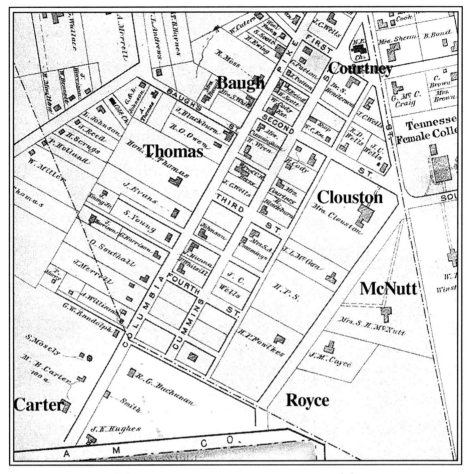

🎗️Franklin, Tennessee🎗️

OLD MAP OF FRANKLIN SHOWING THE PROPERTIES
OF THE THREE FAMILIES MENTIONED IN THE
EARLY CHAPTERS — ROYCE, MCNUTT, AND CARTER.
ALSO SHOWS THE HOME OF THE CLOUSTONS, WHO
ACCOMPANIED THE ROYCES PART OF THE WAY ON
THEIR JOURNEY FROM FRANKLIN TO GREENEVILLE,
TN. NOTE THE COLUMBIA TURNPIKE RUNNING
DIAGONALLY FROM LOWER LEFT TO UPPER RIGHT.
Image courtesy of the Williamson County Historical Society

❧ Table of Contents ❧

❧ Introduction ❧

MENTION THE CIVIL WAR TO MOST FOLKS and they conjure up Lee and Grant, Lincoln and Jefferson Davis, Gettysburg and Appomattox. Most of what we learn in history classes deals with dates and places, generals and battles.

But aside from the fictionalized *Gone With The Wind,* we know little about the very real effects of that war on the farms, villages, towns, and families from which most of the soldiers had come.

Although it sacrificed thousands of sons, brothers, and husbands, the North was largely spared any great physical destruction from the conflict. Northern homes were secure, and families remained where they had settled.

Such was not the case in the South, however, where virtually all the fighting took place. There, towns and cities were sometimes repeatedly captured and retaken in the ebb and flow of battle. The countryside was laid waste, the infrastructure destroyed, and families uprooted. There was no Red Cross, no Salvation Army, no government program to help families recover. Citizens were on their own to get through the war as best they could with the help of family, friends, and neighbors. They then turned to the daunting task of rebuilding their shattered lives when the bloodletting finally ceased.

This book tells the true story of one such family: the Royces of Franklin, Tennessee. It was the extraordinary courage, faith and determination of Martha Broyles Royce which enabled her family to survive the war.

❧ Meet the Royces ❧

FRANKLIN IS ABOUT TWENTY-TWO MILES SOUTH of Nashville in Middle Tennessee. At the time of the Civil War, it was a relatively small town on the Harpeth River. The Royce family owned a four-acre plot on the southern edge of the town, not far from the Columbia Turnpike, the main road that runs from north to south (see map in front of book).

Reverend Moses Strong Royce was born in the North. His family lived in Rutland, Vermont, where Moses' father died when the boy was just eleven years old. A serious scholar, Moses graduated from the University of Vermont at eighteen. He seemed predisposed to poor health, and his mother thought it best for him to seek the more moderate climate of the South. He moved to Greeneville, Tennessee, where he took a job as principal of a boys' school while he studied to prepare for the Episcopal ministry.

Dr. James Broyles, who owned the Walnut Hill plantation, was a member of the board of Moses' school. While visiting Walnut Hill, Moses met Martha, one of Dr. Broyles' daughters. A romance developed and the couple got married.

Upon being ordained, Moses took the position of rector at St. Paul's Episcopal Church in Franklin. However, the small church was not able to pay him a sufficient salary, and at the time of the war he was working as a bookkeeper for the Nashville & Decatur Railroad.

The Royces had two daughters, Betsey and Sally. Betsey, the older of the two, was seven years old when the Civil War started, while her younger sister was just five. Betsey was a seeker after knowledge, like her father, while Sally loved animals and the outdoors, and was more of a determined free spirit, like her mother.

The story you are about to read was written by an adult Betsey. Like most Southern children of the Civil War era, she was forced to grow up very quickly as the fighting engulfed her family. Martha Royce and her daughters were exiled from Franklin for the crime of spying on the Union army, and spent over two years as refugees. The story of the Royces is a chronicle of an extraordinary woman who, contrary to her genteel Southern upbringing, was forced to show amazing strength of character and fortitude in the absence of the man in her life.

Betsey Royce is my maternal grandmother. She was a member of the first class at Wellesley College in 1875, and while there she wrote a narrative of her experiences as a young girl during the Civil War. With her mother's help, she included full dialogue and details about the many unusual characters and situations which the family encountered. Although she writes of her childhood, Grandmother was twenty-one or twenty-two at the time of writing, and her perspective and language are those of an adult.

The original manuscript passed to my mother upon Betsey's death and lay dormant among our family heirlooms. However, I heard about it every once in a while during my own childhood, especially if I complained about some real or imagined hardship.

"If you think you have a difficult time, just remember what your Grandmother Royce went through when she was your age!"

Mother would then recite some incident from Grandmother's story. This always left me feeling properly chastened, and ashamed that I had dared to register my comparatively insignificant complaint!

After I had children of my own, certain incidents would sometimes remind me of those long-ago war stories. I became interested in bringing Grandmother's story to light and sharing it with others. The few people to whom I showed portions of the manuscript urged me to have it published. But the quick passage of time and the dailyness of pursuing my career as a professional artist kept pushing "Betsey's Story" back into the limbo of "things to do someday."

My own grandmother-hood has finally done the trick. I want my grandchildren to meet the Royce family, which represents countless thousands of Southern Civil War families. There may be families today who are struggling against different hardships, and who may take inspiration from reading how one family persevered despite extreme challenges.

As a former teacher, I know how important it is to share the wisdom and experiences of past generations with present ones. It seems especially appropriate to understand the often overlooked civilian side of the Civil War in view of the impending sesquicentennial of that extraordinary event in our nation's history.

A Genteel Spy is Grandmother Betsey's legacy to you. I hope you enjoy the Royce's true story as much as I have enjoyed bringing it to you.

Judith Riker Damon

Roanoke, Virginia—2009

NOTE: I have used the original words as much as possible, editing here and there only for clarity, brevity, or continuity. It needs to be understood that this is the language of the South in the 1860s, and may not always seem sensitive or correct by today's standards. It is, however, historically accurate.

A Genteel Spy

Dedicated

to

children,

the innocent victims

of all wars.

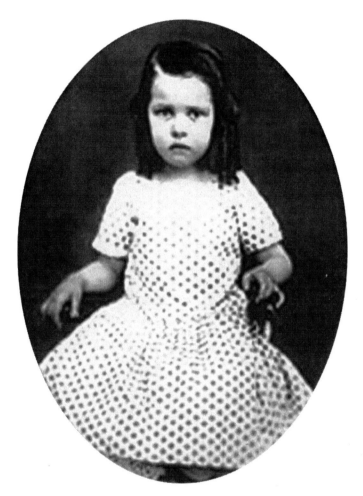

BETSEY ROYCE, AGE 6, 1860

BETSEY ROYCE, AGE 16, 1870

SALLY ROYCE, AGE 14

MARTHA BROYLES ROYCE

REV. MOSES STRONG ROYCE

WALNUT HILL — THE BROYLES' PLANTATION HOUSE

DR. JAMES BROYLES — OWNER, WALNUT HILL

Chapter One
🙰 The Mysterious "It" 🙰

"IT NEVER CAN REACH US."

"You're mistaken. We're going to be in the very midst of it."

Betsey Royce looked up, her attention caught by the urgency of the speakers. She was seven years old and the talk of grown-ups had begun to interest her, especially when it seemed to be so very earnest. In this case the speakers were her parents, the time the spring of 1861, and the place Franklin, Tennessee.

Moses Royce, Betsey's father and the first speaker, was a man of thirty with the temperament of an idealist and dreamer, and the mind of a perpetual student. Although he had come to Franklin to assume the pastorate of St. Paul's Episcopal Church, Moses soon found the salary too small to support a growing family, and was currently employed by the Nashville & Decatur Railroad Company as a bookkeeper in their Nashville office, twenty miles to the north. The railroad ran along the eastern edge of the Royce's four-acre property in Franklin. Betsey was her father's girl in temperament and scholarly interests.

Betsey's mother, Martha Royce, was the very opposite of her husband. The slender grace of her figure, the delicacy of her features, and her curly blond hair might give the careless observer an impression of fragile femininity. But as subsequent events would prove, she was in reality a finely-tempered steel blade sheathed in a scabbard of white velvet. It was she who was certain that "It" would soon be in the family's midst. Sally, Betsey's five-year-old younger sister, shared her mother's independent spirit and love of the outdoors and animals.

What was the mysterious "It" about which the Royce parents so clearly disagreed? Betsey had seen pictures in *Harper's Weekly* of soldiers fighting, and it did not take her long to figure out that "It" must be the fighting, which at that time seemed so far away. The news that Fort Sumter had fallen seemed to prove her conclusion, and Betsey wondered how many cannon balls it had taken to make the fort fall.

One fine Sunday morning that spring, the Royce family prepared to go to church. The best part of going to church for Betsey and Sally was putting on pretty clothes.

They were always dressed alike, and they giggled when people thought they were twins. But giggling was never done inside the church. The girls knew they had to be especially good, since their father was a former minister at St. Paul's and their mother told them they must show other children proper church behavior.

Sitting still was much harder for Sally than it was for Betsey. There was always plenty for Betsey to look at, from all the pretty clothes to the light coming through the windows. She was beginning to listen to see how much she could understand, whether it was the sermon, hymns, or prayers.

Suddenly, a phrase she had not heard before got her attention: "...that it may please Thee with Thy favor to uphold and bless Thy servant, the President of the Confederate States." She

THE MYSTERIOUS "IT"

THIS MORNING BETSEY HEARD SOMETHING
SHE HAD NEVER HEARD BEFORE:
"...THAT IT MAY PLEASE THEE WITH THY
FAVOR TO HOLD AND BLESS THY SERVANT THE
PRESIDENT OF THE CONFEDERATE STATES."

thought about it on the way home but never had a chance to ask her parents what it meant. In time she heard it so often that she no longer wondered about it.

In the following days, Mother kept the girls busy with chores, and it seemed as if Moses' feeling had been right; that the mysterious "It" would not reach Franklin. Betsey began to see more and more fighting pictures in *Harper's* magazine and saw it described as a "Civil War." The thing that puzzled her was the identity of the enemy and what her parents would do if the war did come to Franklin.

Learning to sew was the hardest of Betsey's chores, especially when it was a really hot day. Her fingers would slip when she tried to push the needle through material that resisted strongly. One day, when it was really, really hot, she couldn't stand it any longer and she took the red thread meant for her doll's apron and threw it on the wood pile.

Her mother may not have noticed the red thread on the wood pile, but she did notice that a prize would be given at the county fair for the best pair of stockings knit by a little girl under the age of ten.

"I will get you the needles and yarn," said her mother. "If you are to finish in time for the fair you must get started quickly." Betsey knew better than to say she didn't want to knit the stockings. She sighed as it looked as if it would take her *forever* to do even one stocking.

Little did Betsey or her mother know that the stockings would never be finished. A country at war would fling thoughts about county fair prizes even farther away than the red thread on the wood pile.

Autumn passed and Christmas came and went as usual, but Betsey could see that her parents were more anxious about the war as it got closer and closer to Franklin. It looked as if her mother was right after all (mothers usually are), and they would end up in the midst of the fighting.

As her family left St. Paul's church one Sunday in February, Betsey heard people on the street calling out, "Fort Donelson has surrendered to the Yankee commander, General Grant!" She knew that Fort Donelson was close to Nashville, and Nashville was *very* close to Franklin—and that was scary! Sally held

Betsey's hand tightly as they walked on ahead. Betsey told her not to worry because their friends in Franklin would not let the Yankees hurt them.

Betsey knew things that Sally didn't know. She knew the war was between the Yankees, who lived in the North, and the Confederates, or Rebels — people like themselves — who lived in the South. The hardest thing for Betsey to understand was how her grandparents way up north in Vermont could be Yankees. She knew her father loved his parents and, although Betsey didn't know them very well, she liked to look at their portraits in the living room. She just couldn't think of them as the enemy.

Betsey also thought about her mother's parents who lived in Greeneville, Tennessee. They had a big house that they named Walnut Hill, with slaves who worked in the house and in the fields. The slaves seemed happy, and she knew her grandfather took good care of them. Her mother was supposed to take two slaves with her when she got married, but decided not to, saying she wanted to do her own work — another sign of her mother's fierce independence. Betsey always thought it would have been nice if they had slaves, so she could do the things she *wanted* to do instead of the things she *had* to do.

After they got home from church one Sunday, Moses told them he would have to go to Nashville to help at the railroad station, since he was also the head ticket agent. It was very busy, with everyone trying to leave to get farther away from the Yankees.

In a few days, Moses was back, and he told them how crowded

the trains were. Women, children and older people were in a panic trying to escape the city while they still could. The family watched the trains go by their house. Finally, Moses said, "Look at that train carefully, girls, for it is the last one you will see for a long, long time." Betsey and Sally kept looking, even after the train had disappeared, leaving a trail of smoke behind. From then on they could play on the tracks, which had always been forbidden.

Moses had a surprise for Martha when he returned from his last trip to Nashville. He was able to arrange to salvage all kinds of food and supplies that the Confederate government gave away, rather than leave it for the Yankees. The next morning, two wagons loaded with boxes and barrels drove up to the door. In the first barrel was flour; in another, molasses. There was a bale of cotton and another barrel they thought was more flour. Except it wasn't flour — it was sugar.

"I told you so," Sally said.

Betsey looked at Sally and grinned. "I knew it was sugar, too. I just didn't let on."

"Well," said Martha, "it may be sugar, but the rain got to it and now we have to dry it out. We'll spread it out on sheets upstairs in the attic where it can dry."

Betsey thought that she, Sally, and their mother looked like a train of ants, each carrying a big wet lump of sugar to put on the sheets. When they were finally done, the girls agreed they didn't care if they *ever* saw another bit of sugar! (Of course, they couldn't help taking a taste now and then as they made many trips up the stairs, so it was no surprise that their attraction to sugar was at least temporarily satiated.)

THE MYSTERIOUS "IT"

After the sugar had dried, the girls helped hide the sugar, flour, and molasses so the Yankees couldn't find anything if they should search the house. Moses told Betsey and Sally what had happened in Nashville after Fort Donelson had fallen. People tried to keep the Yankees from getting pounds of bacon, bales of cotton, and other supplies by dumping it all in the Cumberland River. The Yankees found out about it and fished everything out. Betsey hoped their hiding places were good ones and that everything they hid would be safe.

After all the excitement about Fort Donelson's capture, life in Franklin seemed pretty quiet. Spring of 1862 arrived, and Betsey loved to lie in bed each morning until she was called for breakfast. She could look out her window and see a little crabapple tree that she always thought of as "her" tree. It was so pretty when its buds opened up into pink and white blossoms that later turned into rosy toy apples.

One morning, Moses came into their bedroom and said, "If you want to see the Blue Coats, get up and come to the window."

Betsey and Sally's room was on the first floor, so it was easy for them to jump out of bed and race to the dining room window, which had a great view of the Columbia Turnpike. Lines of men in blue uniforms marched as far as the girls could see. Betsey and Sally were thrilled to see them, even though they knew they were looking at the enemy. When Moses promised to take them across Carter's field for a closer look, they hurried to get dressed and eat breakfast.

"Where is Mother?" they asked as they started to eat breakfast. Moses was slow to answer and seemed worried when he told them she had already eaten and was busy upstairs. Breakfast was over quickly, and the girls ran to put on their hoods and capes.

Moses said to Betsey, "Why don't you see if your mother would like to go with us?"

Betsey ran upstairs and into the front room, where she found her mother sitting in front of an open window, a pencil and paper beside her on the windowsill. She was looking through a pair of field glasses at the moving line of blue soldiers on the road beyond Carter's field. From time to time, she wrote numbers on the paper, hardly taking her eyes from the field glasses.

"Mother..." Betsey began.

Lowering the glasses, her mother turned to look at her, and Betsey could tell from her mother's face that she was too excited about what she was doing to stop and come with them. Betsey had no way of knowing that her mother was spying for the Confederate army, and that she herself would be helping her.

"Tell your father I can't come."

Martha then turned back to her work. When Betsey gave her father the message, she thought he looked concerned. Leaving their mother to continue her counting, they went out across Carter's field, which two years later would be thick with graves, but where, on that day, cattle grazed on fresh new grass.

Moses, Betsey, and Sally stood by the Columbia Turnpike where the ranks in blue were quickly passing. It was General Don Carlos Buell's army on a forced march to join General Ulysses S. Grant's army at Shiloh. While Betsey recognized that she was seeing the enemy for the first time, whereas she had only before seen them as pictures in *Harper's*, she did not feel the fear or hatred which she thought a little Southerner *should* feel. In fact, she felt real admiration as she gazed at the gallant army, its brand new uniforms, its shining arms, and its un-thinned ranks. Each regiment passed to the sound of martial music, which seemed to move them faster toward Shiloh.

Although in years to come the Royces were to see many marching armies—the Blues *and* the Grays—never again would they behold one so brave and fine in appearance. Dinner was late that night, for Martha stopped counting only when the supply wagons appeared.

Chapter Two
✾ Within the Lines ✾

FROM THEN ON, LIFE FOR BETSEY AND HER FAMILY was never the same. Something unusual was always happening. Troops, sometimes wearing the gray but more often the blue, seemed to take turns occupying their pretty little town. Betsey couldn't believe what happened on one really crazy day! The Yankees made cooking campfires for breakfast, then marched off on their patrols. While they were gone, the boys in gray moved in and used the same fires to cook lunch. Then they moved back to their previous positions, and the blue-clad soldiers returned to cook supper, using those same fires.

It was really hard for Betsey and Sally to play when so much was happening around them. Martha suggested they make a playhouse over the outside north window of their house, but it was too windy there.

To make matters worse, Fort Granger had been built across the Harpeth River on Figure's Bluff (see pg. 197), and gunners would practice firing over the Royce's house into Carter's field! Since there was no way they could stop the guns from firing, the girls learned to play with one eye on the fort. Whenever they saw a puff of smoke, they would run inside the house before the shells passed over. They did this so often they became very good at dodging the firing.

It was August, and the little toy apples on the crabapple tree Betsey loved so much were almost ripe. She woke up one night to hear her parents talking.

Moses was saying, "I had hoped to stay with you and the children, but there's no way I can do that with so many joining the army. When my company is complete I will join Colonel Starnes."

"How soon will that be?" asked Martha.

Betsey listened anxiously for Moses' answer. When she heard "within ten days," Betsey felt a big lump in her throat. How could they get along without their father?

The next thing she heard was Moses asking if Martha could make his uniform. "Oh, I'm sure I can," Martha said. "I can rip up an old jacket for the pattern, and pantaloons are not very difficult. I'll get Betsey to sew on the trim."

When Betsey heard that she would have a part in making her father's uniform, she wished she had worked harder on her sewing.

"I just hate to leave you and the girls here alone," Moses said, "especially since you are so far away from your own family."

"But remember, Moses, my sister Julia and her husband William are here," said Martha.

"That is not much comfort to me," Moses replied. "They will stay just long enough for William to complete his business before going to your parents' home in Greeneville. I wish you and the girls would go with them."

Betsey hoped so, too, since she loved visiting her grandparents.

"Oh, I could never do that," Martha said. "How could I go and leave behind all that we have in the world? I must stay and protect our house as best I can."

While her parents talked far into the night, Betsey fell asleep.

For the next two weeks, things were quiet in Franklin. No Gray troops and no Blue ones. It was a good time for Martha to work on Moses' uniform. Betsey felt very proud when both her mother and father told her how well she had sewn the red braid on the gray shirts.

Betsey loved the way her father looked when he was ready to leave, mounted on his gray horse in his new gray uniform. But she could hardly bear to say good-bye. As Moses pulled Betsey into his arms, he whispered in her ear, "I'm counting on you to help your mother and take care of Sally for me. I will come back as soon as I can." Just like the time they had watched the train disappear, Sally and Betsey watched their father ride down the road until he was a tiny speck and then could no longer be seen.

It was hard to get used to not having her father at home. Now that he was gone, Betsey realized how many times she had gone to him when she wanted something explained. Sometimes her mother was too busy to go into much detail or answer more questions. Even though Betsey was Sally's age when her father became the minister of St. Paul's, she remembered how she loved seeing him in the front of the church, leading their friends and neighbors in prayers and hymns. *Maybe that's the reason Father's name is Moses,* she thought, *because he led people in worshiping God.*

Betsey would try to do what she had promised her father: to help her mother and to take care of Sally. But she would be *so* happy when he came home to stay.

As Martha, Sally, and Betsey gradually got used to life without Moses, more Blue soldiers moved into Franklin. The only times they saw the Gray soldiers were during a few daring raids. Once, as Martha, Betsey, and Sally watched from a window as the Grays were being chased out of town, they saw the color-bearer throw down the Confederate flag and ride for his life. Betsey couldn't believe what she had seen.

"Oh, Mother," she cried, "let me run out and pick it up."

"Look! Look!" Martha exclaimed, and Betsey turned back to the window, holding her breath to see what would happen. A soldier riding behind the scared color-bearer ordered him to pick up the flag, but the man only galloped away faster. The other soldier got off his horse, picked up the trampled flag, remounted and, standing up in his stirrups, walked his horse down the road waving the battle flag until the last possible minute. Then, putting spurs to his horse, he made a mad dash to join his comrades, the brilliant battle flag streaming out behind him.

It was something Betsey never forgot.

One of Betsey and Sally's chores was to drive their two cows out past the pickets (see Appendix) posted at the edge of the pasture.

WITHIN THE LINES

SHE WOULD PUT A MESSAGE INSIDE THE HEM OF
BETSEY'S DRESS AND INSTRUCT HER TO TELL THE
MISTRESS OF THE HOUSE, "TAKE ME INTO YOUR
BEDROOM AND OPEN THE HEM OF MY DRESS."

They frequently carried pies and cookies, which their mother instructed them to share with the soldiers. Betsey noticed that many fences had been torn down to feed the campfires, but their fence was as good as ever. When she asked her mother about it, she was told that as long as she and Sally gave the soldiers some of the things she baked, their fences would not be touched. Betsey thought she was a pretty smart mother.

Many of the pickets came by the Royce's kitchen to boil their coffee. Even if they were the enemy, most of these Yankees were friendly and talked to them almost like Moses used to do. There was one soldier they really didn't like because he sat in a corner pretending to read, but Betsey could see that he was watching her mother very closely. When he came, they were careful not to talk too much.

Betsey knew that her mother had been doing all she could to help the Confederates. She also knew that the Yankees thought her mother was passing information to other ladies in Franklin, who then passed it along to the Confederate army. Many times, Martha would use Betsey to carry a message to Mrs. McNutt or one of the other Franklin ladies. She would put a message inside the hem of Betsey's dress and instruct her to tell the mistress of the house, "Take me into your bedroom and open the hem of my dress."

Betsey felt very important every time she carried a message. Best of all, she hoped she was helping her father come home sooner!

WITHIN THE LINES

To celebrate Christmas, Aunt Julia, Uncle William, and the cousins came from across town to visit the Royces. There were very few presents. When Christmas was over, Betsey and Sally did not see their cousins for several months. More and more Blue soldiers came into Franklin, and they were no longer friendly.

The winter of 1862-63 was really hard for Sally and Betsey. They never saw their friends, and hardly ever a neighbor. Sally asked her mother if this was what it felt like to be a prisoner. Martha smiled and said, "Almost, Sally, but be thankful we're in our own home."

One of the hardest things was keeping track of the days of the week. Every day seemed the same. They had to listen carefully for the church bells so they knew it was Sunday.

Once in a while, it was good to see Mr. McNutt, their closest neighbor. He always had news to give them, but nothing that made them feel better. That was especially true when he insisted they should have a guard posted inside the house to protect them from the bad behavior of the Yankee soldiers. Martha was not happy about having a stranger in her house, but the girls were looking forward to having something different to think about, even if it was the enemy. They were surprised and delighted with their first guard, who was only sixteen and just getting used to being a soldier. Betsey had a lot of fun talking with him and asking questions about life in the North.

The next guard was a disappointment to the girls, since he was German and said hardly anything they could understand. He was able to talk a little with Martha, and he seemed very happy to be with them.

Betsey and Sally were delighted with their final guard, a fun-loving young man. He played outside with the girls — Hide and Seek and other games. Betsey was so happy when their new friend was mistakenly allowed to remain on duty for several extra days. It felt good to have a friend, even for a short time, and even if he was the enemy.

Then one night Martha said, "They have taken away our guard." Betsey was thankful it was dark and her mother could not see the tears rolling down her cheeks. She knew she was not supposed to cry for a soldier who wore a blue uniform, but their friendship meant more to her than the color he was wearing.

One cold night in February, Martha, Betsey, and Sally sat quietly by a cheerful fire in their living room. Martha was reading aloud from a book on the history of the United States. Some of it was hard to understand, but Martha told the girls to stand on mental tiptoes and they would do better. Before long it was time to tuck in their dolls, Belle and Rose, and go to bed. As they were getting into their nightgowns, they were surprised by a loud knock at the door. Martha took the light and breathlessly hastened to the door, followed by Betsey and Sally.

"What is it?" Martha asked without opening the door.

"Open the door! We have orders to search this house," a man's voice replied.

"Can you come back in the daytime?" Martha answered, hoping to gain time. "It is late and I am alone."

"If you don't open the door, we will break it down!" came the stern reply.

"Very well, just wait a minute," Martha said as she ran upstairs to open a window and call for help, as the guards had told her to do.

But instead of receiving help from friendly guards, she found their house surrounded by soldiers with their guns pointed in the direction of the house. There was more banging on the door, followed by a loud voice threatening again to break down the door. Betsey shivered with fear, which was made worse when she looked at her mother, whose face was white and whose hands were shaking.

Oh, thought Betsey, *how I wish Father was home.* Martha took a deep breath and then called to the soldiers, "Give me time to dress and I will open the door."

When she finished dressing, she said to Betsey, "Put on a dark dress and when I go to open the door I will take the light with me, leaving this part of the house in darkness. Then you must slip out the back door and go across to Mr. McNutt's. Ask him to come quickly. He has told me to call him if I need help, and we need it now. Sally, you get in bed and keep quiet."

Betsey said, "Yes, Mother, I'll go." And in a moment she had slipped into her dark dress. Now she stood waiting until her mother had carried the light away before starting off through the night on her important errand. In the days before Fort Sumter fell, when life was peaceful, Betsey liked stories about Africa and all the wild animals living there. They seemed so real to her that she often thought she saw them in dark corners of rooms or on the stairs and was afraid. But now that her life was turned upside down by war, she was ready to go out alone, into the cold darkness without a thought of fear.

Martha took up the candle and went to the front door, her face white and stern. Betsey tiptoed out of the bedroom toward the back door. Her eyes were blind in the darkness, and she heard the clatter of rain falling against the windows. Groping her way to the door, she laid her hand on the knob, took a deep breath, and opened the door. Her foot was on the first step when the cry "Halt!" rang in her ears.

She heard the sharp rattle of guns being brought to position and quickly realized the door was guarded. Jumping back, she slammed and locked it, then ran to her place in bed beside Sally, not stopping to undress.

"I couldn't get out," she whispered to her sister. "Let's pull up the covers and pretend to be asleep." So Betsey and Sally lay close together, whispering in the dark and listening intently for sounds from the rest of the house.

Meanwhile, Martha, candle in hand, had opened the door to an officer, who was backed up by five or six soldiers who filed in and stood in the hall, rain dripping from their rubber coats. Outside, a guard had been stationed at each door and window to prevent the escape of anyone who might be hiding inside.

Martha felt better after she realized that the officer's only purpose was to search the house for spies. She quickly led the men from room to room, pointing out closets and nooks they might overlook.

When they reached the living room where the two dolls, Belle and Rose, were snuggly tucked into their bed, the officer took the candle from Martha and stood looking down at them, perhaps thinking of a little girl back home who might have put her own dolls to bed. After spending the same amount of time looking down at Betsey and Sally, who pretended to be asleep, the officer stopped in the front hall and said to Martha, "I wish to thank you, madam, for your courtesy."

"In return," she replied, "I would like to offer you a word of advice. The next time it is your duty to search a house where a woman is alone, try to do it in the daytime."

He bowed quietly and closed the door behind him.

Two weeks later, a soldier stood outside with orders from the Yankee General Charles Gilbert in his hand. Betsey wondered what was in the orders. She watched her mother's face anxiously, and when her mother explained what was going to happen, Betsey felt better.

Yankee officers were going to live in their house with them. Martha, who would never let anyone else in her kitchen, would do the cooking. That afternoon, their house was filled as it had never been filled before. Living with the officers made Betsey remember how much fun they had had with the special guard whom she would never forget. It was hard for Betsey to understand how she could fear the "Blue Coats" so much, while at the same time liking some of the people who wore them.

Of all the officers in the house, there were three that Betsey thought were special, but she decided not to talk about them to her mother. She had a feeling her mother might not understand why she was wasting her time thinking about Yankees.

The first officer who got her attention was, of course, General Gilbert. He was more like a grandfather than a soldier—very gentle when he spoke, polite and kind. Betsey couldn't imagine being afraid of him.

A second officer to win Betsey's heart was young Lieutenant Van Arden, who was handsome, fun-loving and well-mannered. Betsey loved his beautiful blue silk neckties, and he made her feel special by his friendly greetings and pats on the head when she held the dining room doors open as the officers left.

The third officer to make an impression on Betsey was Colonel McLean, who was very different from the other two. He was not at all kind or friendly, and Betsey and Sally did not try to talk to him. His family was famous for fighting hard. Colonel McLean hated the South and everyone who fought for the South. Betsey hoped he would not stay in their house as long as the other officers.

Betsey especially did not like Colonel McLean during meal-time, when he and her mother would fight each other with words. The colonel would say things like, "You'd better hope your hus-band comes home from the army or you will find yourself and the children heading south in ten days."

Martha's answer came quickly: "I will go into the army myself before that happens!" When Betsey heard that, she nearly dropped the plate of biscuits she was passing.

Another time, the colonel talked about Buell's army. "When I arrived here", he said, "yours was the first name reported to me as a spy and informer. I was told you counted Buell's army as it passed through."

"That is quite true. I did," said Martha.

"What number did you get?" he demanded scornfully.

"Thirty thousand," Martha said.

"Allow me to say that you missed if by half," the colonel sneered.

"I was correct, for others besides myself counted and we agreed as to numbers."

"That would be impossible," the colonel said, "for we purposely marched our men by different roads in order to prevent counting."

"Yes, but there was a Southern woman on each road, and we compared notes afterward," replied Martha with a gleam in her eye.

Betsey was very thankful when the kindly General Gilbert told her mother how good the coffee was and could he please have another cup.

Betsey, Sally, and Martha had no way of knowing that while their house was being taken over by the Yankee officers, their father had almost come home. Since joining the Southern army, his duty was to scout the countryside around Franklin, and particularly the gun boats on the Cumberland river. One night he was quite close to Franklin and, being anxious about his family, he slipped through enemy lines and got within sight of his house. But much to his surprise and shock, the once quiet, dark house was lighted from top to bottom, with sentries posted and Yankee officers coming and going. There was nothing for him to do but crawl away with a heavy heart, even more worried about his wife and two little girls.

At the end of the week, the officers left, and Betsey had a good time going into the rooms they had vacated to see if there was anything they had forgotten. In the general's room she found two treasures — a box of matches and a jar of potted shrimp. The box of matches would be useful, but she had no idea what could be done with potted shrimp, never having had shrimp to eat. Betsey was not surprised when her mother told her to put it in the pantry because she might find a way to use it — and, in time, Betsey found that her mother was right.

Chapter Three
❧ The Clash Of Arms ❧

THE LONG WINTER OF 1862–63 PASSED with the coming of April's warm weather to enjoy. Martha and the girls decided to plant a garden. Their faithful helper, Donny, who worked on a neighboring farm, was there to get the ground ready for the seeds that had been carefully saved from the past summer.

Donny said with a big grin, "Guess you don't have to worry 'bout the chickens scratchin' up the seeds, cause there's no more chickens! The Yankees got 'em all."

"You're so right, Donny," said Martha. "It's nice you can find something good about the Yankees getting our chickens. When you're done with that row you can go home. The girls and I will finish up."

When the garden was planted in neat rows, Betsey and Sally felt good that the chore was done and started chasing each other around the outside of the house. In a moment they were back again, excitement on their faces and in their voices.

"Mother, Mother!" they cried. "Just come and see how Mr. Carter's Negroes are running." Martha hurried after the children and, just as they had described, the slaves who had been plowing Carter's field had left their work and were running wildly toward the cotton gin, trying to find shelter. Martha did not have far to look for the reason. To her left, she saw a long line of Confederate cavalry leaving the Columbia Turnpike and arranging themselves in battle formation across the end of Carter's wide field, facing the town.

In a moment, Martha realized what was going to happen. Turning to the girls she said, "We must hurry indoors and lock up the house. There is going to be a fight!" Together they ran inside and quickly closed the house up tight. Then they ran upstairs to the room facing Carter's field so they could watch the battle.

"Mother!" cried Betsey. "See how the pickets are running." As the pickets ran past the house they called out, wanting shelter. But no door was open to them, so they ran on, jumping through the Osage hedge and climbing over the plant fence separating the Royce's lot from Mr. McNutt's.

"I'm sure they must have torn their clothes," said Sally. "The hedge is awful thorny." As their mother and the girls watched, a long cavalry line formed. Then they rode toward the town, shouting their famous rebel yell, their long hair streaming out behind them in the wind. The three watching at the window were so excited that they threw open the window and waved frantically to the soldiers in gray passing by. This was what they had been waiting for during all the time the Yankees had taken over the town and their home.

Zip! Zip! Zip!

The leaden Minie balls (*see* Appendix) came zinging and pelting against the front of the house. Martha drew back from the window and looked across the field, for the bullets were coming at right angles to the line of the charge. They could not be aimed at the soldiers who already had passed on into town. What she

"WE CAN'T STAY HERE," MOTHER CRIED TO
BETSEY AND SALLY ABOVE THE NOISE.
"WE MUST GET DOWN TO THE CELLAR
OR WE SHALL BE KILLED."

saw was a reserve guard of about fifty Union soldiers stationed across Carter's field, beyond the Confederate charge and close by Mr. Carter's house. These men were facing her house, and their leveled guns were firing directly at her!

"Come away, children!" she cried, "or we shall all be killed! The reserves are firing on us!"

Just then a ball struck the iron hinge on the inside window shutter and left it hanging crooked, then glanced across the room, striking the other wall. Trembling, they went to another room where they held tight to each other, not knowing what to expect next. All they could hear were the guns from the nearby fort as they began to roar, along with other strange sounds filling the air.

"We can't stay here," Martha cried to Betsey and Sally above the noise. "We must get down to the cellar or we shall be killed. We will go down one at a time, so that if one is hurt the other can look after her. Sally, you go first, then Betsey and I will come last."

Going into the hall, they stood at the top of the second floor stairs. It was very hard to send a little girl of six alone down the stairs to face the rain of bullets, but there was no other way.

"Go, Sally!" her mother commanded, placing her on the top step. Sally took just two steps when the wall ripped open just in front of her. Sally screamed in terror and raced back to her mother's arms.

"I can't, I can't," she cried, "I'm so afraid, I just can't."

"You *must*!" Martha said sternly, turning Sally around to face the stairs. At that point, Betsey stepped forward and took Sally's hand.

"Don't be afraid, Sally," she said as bravely as she could. "We'll go down together."

With that assurance, the two girls raced down the stairs to the first floor hallway, with Martha right behind. The girls hurried into the kitchen and huddled next to the fireplace while Martha opened the cellar door, which was part of the kitchen floor.

"Hurry and get in the cellar. You will be safe there," she called to them. "Now go!"

With newfound courage, Sally hurried down the steep steps. Betsey followed quickly, then Martha, and in a few moments they were all safe in the protective cellar. Even then, Martha was not quiet for long. The muffled booming of the cannon made her think that a shell might strike the house and set it afire, which made her more anxious and uneasy. Finally, she told the girls what was on her mind.

"If a shell were to strike the house, it could burn down over us before we had a chance to save ourselves. We might just as well be shot as burned to death! I am going up to keep watch."

"Mother, don't go. You'll be killed!" pleaded little Sally, beginning to cry again.

"If you must go, let me go with you," urged Betsey, frightened but composed.

"No, neither of you shall come," Martha replied. "You are safer where you are, but I need to watch for anything that might cause the house to catch fire. I'm always within calling distance if you need me."

"Mother," Betsey said to her when she returned the second

time, "just now we heard something strike the pipe outside the cellar wall, and then there was a dreadful groan."

"Perhaps some wounded man has crawled under the house for safety," she replied. "We will look for him after the battle is over."

So saying, Martha returned above to continue her watch.

In the hour that followed, Martha saw horrid things, new and strange in her experience. Mounted men, both Blue and Gray, charged wildly around her house; Minies ripped through its walls as though the walls were made of cardboard; shells fell and exploded, sending their deadly rain in all directions. She saw one man fall, his head blown off.

The air was full of smoke and dust and strange noises, and the cries and shouts of men mingled with the rushing sound of horses' hooves. "The horrid din of war," which she had once thought of only as a figure of speech, became in that hour a grim reality to her.

During the noise and confusion, Martha thought she heard the sound of a child's voice crying for help from outside. When she saw it was a boy about twelve years old, she quickly opened the door. At first, Martha did not recognize Jimmy Ward, a neighbor's son. His eyes were round and bulging with terror, and his freckled face was pale from all he had seen. By the time Jimmy had finished telling Martha about the danger he had escaped, though, he was feeling much better. Martha became very interested when Jimmy told her about all the guns that were lying on the ground out in the field.

"The shooting is almost over, so I can go out and bring some in to you," said Jimmy.

"Oh, yes," Martha answered. "Bring as many as you can. I will hide them in the cellar. But you must be very careful."

Betsey heard her mother talking to someone and thought it was safe to come out of the cellar. But as she started up the stairs, Martha surprised her by saying, "Not yet, Betsey. I am going to hand you some guns to hide in the cellar when Jimmy brings them from the battlefield."

The first weapon was a heavy rifle. "Be careful, Betsey. It might be loaded and could fire accidentally."

Betsey couldn't wait to put the rifle in a corner of the cellar. She didn't like to handle it. It was not the same as hiding the food that her father had brought from Nashville.

Betsey and Sally were so happy to hear their mother tell them it was finally safe to come upstairs. Jimmy was only able to bring Martha a few more guns because the Yankees were out looking for their weapons and getting more and more unhappy when they couldn't find them.

Betsey could tell that something was bothering Jimmy, and it wasn't about the guns. Finally he just blurted it out.

"There's a dead Johnny lying at your front gate, and I think it might be Captain Royce. You should come look at him."

Martha followed Jimmy to the front gate, with Betsey and Sally following slowly, their hearts beating rapidly. *It can't be Father*, Betsey thought with every step she took, *it just can't be.*

Betsey could tell by the way her mother acted when she bent over the soldier at the gate that it was *not* her father. Betsey hugged Sally and wiped the tears from her little sister's face. "It's all right, Sally, that's not Father. He's still alive."

As the girls walked around the dead soldier, Betsey kept Sally close to her, so Sally couldn't see him too well. The only dead person Betsey had ever seen was an old man who looked like he had gone to sleep in the comfort of his own bed; so very different from the poor soldier lying face down on the dusty road. His clothes were course homespun, dyed butternut brown and worn threadbare. The shoes on his feet were old and broken. A pool of blood had formed on the road beneath him. White dust lay on his cheek and in his long, untrimmed black hair.

Betsey looked away with tears in her eyes.

Jimmy, his job done, said, "I think I'd better get along home now. Maw will be worried. I'll come back and see you tomorrow."

"That will be fine, Jimmy. I may need you," Martha answered.

Leaving the dead soldier lying there, they moved on, looking to see what damage had been done to their property. They passed through the hedge separating their front yard from the lot beyond, walking through clover which was quite high. Martha's alert eye caught the shine of a carbine lying half hidden in the clover. She knew she must have it. This was not the time to take it, what with ambulances coming and going, picking up the wounded. She would wait till later. Martha stood over it, letting her crinoline skirt hide it from view until there was less activity on the field.

It was heartbreaking for Martha to look at a field, once so peaceful but now dotted with the bodies of the dead and wounded. Where once she heard the sound of birds, now it was the groans of the injured, the strange noises of crippled horses and the angry voices of passing soldiers that filled the air.

Betsey and Sally came running back to their mother, anxious

to tell her what they had seen. "Mother," cried Sally, "you just ought to come see what they have done to Donny's garden."

"I will in a moment," she replied. "Betsey, come here." As Betsey came close, she continued in a low voice, "You see where I am standing? Look at it well, so you will know exactly how to find it in the dark."

She said no more, but Betsey looked carefully at the spot, noticing the distance and direction from the hedge, then looked up at her mother and nodded. When they moved away, Betsey caught sight of a shiny carbine and partly guessed what was in her mother's mind.

Sally pulled her mother along by the hand until they came to their garden. "Just look what they did to the neat rows. It's a mess. And after all Donny's hard work!"

Martha gave Sally a hug and said, "I feel badly too, dear, especially since it may be a long time before another garden can be planted."

"Come see what I found, Sally," called Betsey. She held out her hand. In it were used Minie balls in all crazy shapes. "Here's one in the shape of a hat." That was all it took for Sally to join Betsey in searching for more used Minie balls. After picking up the ones along the board fence between their land and Mr. McNutt's, they decided there might be interesting ones on the other side. They quickly scrambled over the fence and began looking along the ground. Something much better was spotted by Betsey—a handsome Colt revolver lying by a fence post.

"There's a pistol." whispered Sally, running up to her sister. "Aren't you going to pick it up?"

Betsey shook her head. "No, not now. Someone might see us.

We'll go down the road and look for Minie balls till there's no one around."

Finally, they saw their chance and ran as fast as they could to where the pistol lay. Betsey snatched it up, wrapped it in the skirt of her dress, and fled back to where they had climbed over the fence. Letting Sally go over first, she carefully passed the pistol down to her. Then she jumped over herself and led the way back home.

Martha could hardly believe what they had done when they showed her the Colt revolver. Betsey and Sally were so thrilled with their prize, they wanted to go back out to see what else they could find. Martha was against this, but said that Sally could go out as if to play. Such a little girl would not be suspected.

Sally went back to where they had found the revolver. She sat down and played with pieces of Minie balls. Pretty soon, a Union officer came by, looking at the ground beside the fence. "I'm sure I took off my pistol while I was helping a man into an ambulance, and I'm positive I laid it here by this post," he said. Sally hugged herself. She was so happy they had fooled him.

When Sally ran into the house to tell Betsey and Martha about the officer looking for his gun, she found them in the cellar, hiding the pistol. They had to hurry, because an officer and his men were on their way to search the house. The trap door to the cellar was covered with the same material as the rest of the kitchen floor, and not easily seen. Quickly, Martha placed a rocking chair over the door, placed a shawl over the chair, and had Betsey sit in the rocking chair with Sally kneeling beside her. Martha gave them a picture book to look at until the soldiers left.

As Betsey turned the pages of the book, she whispered to

Sally about how much fun it was to fool the Yankees! After the soldiers left and Sally had gone to bed, Betsey sat with her mother until it was nearly dark outside. The carbine lay out there in the deep clover, waiting for them to retrieve it. Finally, Martha nodded to Betsey, who had put on her dark dress. "Are you ready to go out, Betsey? Do you remember just where it is?"

Betsey nodded.

"We will go out and creep along the hedge until we come opposite the gun. Then you, being the smaller, must crawl through the hedge, find the gun, and drag it back to me. Do you understand?"

"Yes, Mother," Betsey replied, shivering slightly. She was only eight, after all, and the night was dark, with dead bodies not far away. A moment later they were out the back door into the darkness.

All went as Martha had planned until they came to the opening in the hedge. Suddenly, another danger occurred. Two soldiers were riding past. Instinctively, Betsey and Martha crouched closer to the hedge.

"One thing more, Betsey," Martha whispered. "As you go, keep very close to the ground. If your head should be seen against the sky, a passing soldier might shoot you."

Betsey nodded to show she understood, then crept through the hedge and on toward the gun, sliding over the thick clover, which was wet with dew. Some soldiers passed along the road, laughing and talking. She froze flat against the ground until they went by, then began crawling again.

At last, her groping fingers felt the cold steel of the gun. All was quiet, so she returned quickly to Martha with the carbine, and a few minutes later they were safely inside the house. When Betsey climbed into bed beside Sally, she was still chilled and nervous. It took her a while to get to sleep, and the dreams she had were not pleasant.

The next morning, the girls watched from their house as the dead were buried. A deep trench was dug for the horses; another smaller trench for the Confederate dead. For several days after the burial, kind-hearted Southern ladies came out from town, bringing flowers for the graves. Sally watched from a distance, then ran home laughing.

"Mother," she cried, "those nice ladies are crying over the horses."

"Never mind," Martha replied. "They mean well, and how can they tell one grave from another?"

Just then, Betsey burst in. "Mother," she said, "Mrs. Lewis and some other ladies are at the gate. They want to know if you will walk with them down to the graves."

"Tell them 'yes,'" Martha replied, untying her apron. "At least I can keep them from crying over the horses' graves."

The dead had been buried near the road and, as Martha stood talking with her friends, a cavalcade came slowly down the road. It was a general and his staff. As they drew near, Martha saw one of the men speak to the general, who turned around and looked directly at Martha.

"Who is that man?" she asked Mrs. Lewis.

"That is General Gordon Granger," her friend replied. "His

command is stationed here. He will know you when he sees you again," she added, laughing.

"He will indeed," replied Martha, but she was unusually quiet as she walked back with her friends. The intense look the general had given Martha left no doubt that he had been told of her activities as a spy for the Confederate army. After her friends left, Martha walked slowly through the home she had loved and in which she had taken such great pride.

She would not be surprised if she was forced to leave it.

The next day, the expected blow fell. An aide to the general stood at the door, a paper in his hand. He read her an order from General Granger, demanding that she leave Franklin in three days!

"This is short notice," Martha responded, "and I have no one with me but these two little girls. Am I allowed to contact my neighbors and get help from them?"

"Yes", he replied. "That will be permitted. But you must be prepared to leave on the third day, which will be Friday. You may take any household goods you wish, besides your personal belongings."

"I will be ready," she told him. He bowed and left.

Betsey could not believe what she had heard. How could they leave their house in three days, and if they did, when would they come back?

Martha looked at Betsey and said, "I know this is as upsetting to you as it is for me, but we must do everything we can to help Father and the brave men who are fighting for us. We have to leave Franklin and all our friends for now. I promise that when the war is over we will come home. Now, run quickly to Mr. McNutt's and tell him to come at once. I need him."

The good neighbor speedily arrived with deep concern showing all over his face. "Mrs. Royce, ma'am, I can't tell you how sorry I am to hear what Betsey tells me. To think that you have to be out of your house in just three days. You've hardly had time to think about what you will do, where you will go."

Martha smiled at Mr. McNutt. "This is not the surprise to me that it is to you. The Yankees know I've been spying for our cause and they want me out of Franklin. I have thought about what I would do when the orders came to leave my home. I plan to go to Greeneville, my father's home in East Tennessee."

When Betsey heard her mother talk about going to her grandfather's, she felt much better. She loved her grandparents and all the good times they had together.

Mr. McNutt was worried about how they would get to Greeneville, with the railroads torn up and armies camped along the way. "You can't take that journey alone with these two little girls."

"I know you're right," Martha said, "so I am planning to go with my sister and brother-in-law, Mr. Ramsey. They have been planning to go for some time, and now that I am forced to leave we can all go together."

"I am relieved to hear that," Mr. McNutt said. "Now what about your household goods—what are you going to do with them?"

"I shall take nothing except clothing and a few pieces of small silver, mostly prizes I won at the fairs. I want to sell all the furniture," Martha went on, "except for Mr. Royces's books and the portraits of his father and mother, all of which he values highly."

"I can keep the portraits and books at my house," said Mr. McNutt. "And if you want, I can take the portraits now."

"Thank you," replied Martha. "I know they will be in good hands."

Betsey had always loved the portraits of her grandparents. The dark eyes of her namesake grandmother and the deep red dress she wore satisfied Betsey's artistic sense. Sometimes, when no one was around, Betsey would stand in front of her grandmother's portrait and talk to her like she would to Sally or her mother. No matter what she said, her grandmother always smiled at her.

It was scary the day the Minies tore through the house, and one had passed only an inch below Grandmother Betsey's portrait. *Today was even worse*, Betsey thought, as with tearful eyes she watched Mr. McNutt carrying away the beloved portraits. Their home was emptied as people came and bought furniture. Finally, Martha told Betsey and Sally they could each pick one toy to take with them and one toy to share. Belle and Rose were quickly chosen, and a doll's tea set would be shared.

Martha told Sally she would have to let her friend, Alice McNutt, take care of her kitty, Charlie Cat, while they were gone. No one knew why Sally had named him Charlie Cat, but he always answered to his name, and that's what mattered. Sally insisted on keeping Charlie Cat with her as long as she could. Alice would have to wait for him until the family had left Franklin.

The night before they left, Martha asked Jimmy to come to the house after dark. He agreed and thought, *I'll bet it has some-*

thing to do with the guns. When he arrived at the Royce home and saw the shutters closed tightly, he knew he was right.

The guns were laid out on the kitchen table, and when Jimmy saw the carbine and the pistol, he gave a whistle. "I didn't know you had those. They're great—better than the rifles."

"I haven't much time left now," began Martha. "And since I can't take these firearms with me, I want to hide them where they won't be found by the soldiers. In Mr. Royce's study upstairs, there is a manhole in the ceiling. I want you to climb in there and put the guns away under the roof."

"That will be a great place for them," said Jimmy. "Let's get started." Quickly they went upstairs, carrying the guns and a step ladder.

"Shall I bring the pistol, Mother?" asked Sally when she saw it had been left behind.

"No, let that stay," Martha replied. "We will see about it shortly."

Once the guns were hidden under the roof, all four of them came back and sat around the kitchen table, looking at the pistol. "Jimmy," said Martha, "I can't carry all the guns away, but I want to take this pistol."

"Yes, we captured it," Sally piped up.

"All right, Sally, that's enough," her mother told her. Then, turning her attention back to Jimmy, she went on. "I know we will be searched for firearms while we're still within enemy lines. I decided that if they find a part of the pistol, we need to make sure they don't find the rest. Can you take the pistol apart, Jimmy?"

"Indeed I can, ma'am", exclaimed Jimmy. "Get me your tool box and I'll show you."

With the family watching, the pistol was in pieces in record time — the stock and chamber in one piece, the barrel in another, and the screws in a neat little pile.

"Good boy, that's perfect!" said Martha as Jimmy looked up, smiling broadly. "Now let me see if I can do my part as well as you did."

The three children watched her with great interest. She went into her room and returned with a long-netted, beaded purse. Wrapping a dollar bill around the chamber of the pistol, she dropped it into one end of the purse, where it fit exactly. She held it up for them to admire.

"They won't look there," she smiled. Then she went into the pantry and brought out a plate of soft ginger cookies, freshly baked for their journey. Taking the wooden butt of the pistol, which had separated into parts, she laid each part between two cookies and pressed them firmly together.

"They won't look there, either," she commented, and the children laughed with delight. Their mother was inventing the best game yet.

Next, the long barrel of the pistol wormed its way into a loaf of bread, and then only the pile of screws remained. Martha looked at them thoughtfully, then a gleam of fun lighted her face. She disappeared into the pantry again and came back a moment later with the jar of potted shrimp that General Gilbert had left behind.

"I thought this might prove useful sometime," she said, laughing. As she sat at the table to open the jar, the children followed every move. When she began to bury the screws, one by one, in the pasty depth of the shrimp jar, the children thought that was the funniest thing they had ever seen. Sally could hardly stop laughing, and Martha had to remind her and Betsey that they must remember not to laugh when it was part of their lunch basket. The Yankees would wonder why their lunch basket would make them laugh.

When Friday morning came, a carriage and guard stood waiting for them at the gate. There was also a wagon for three trunks and a smaller hat box to hold all that they could take with them. Except for the bedding and a few dishes, the house was empty. Martha locked the door and walked to the gate, the key in her hand.

They had just settled down in the carriage with the lunch basket and two carpet bags, and the driver had taken up the reins, when Sally looked out and saw Charlie Cat. He stood mewing and looking up at her as if to say, "Hey, you forgot me."

Sally burst into tears. "Oh, Mother, Mother, please may I take Charlie Cat? Oh, may I? May I? I won't go without him," she wailed, trying to climb out. As Martha pulled Sally back and tried to comfort her, the horses began to move.

Betsey looked back lovingly at the house she was never to see again. Last of all, her eyes rested on her little crabapple tree, a mass of pink and white blossoms. Her eyes blurred sadly before a bend in the road hid everything familiar from sight.

Chapter Four
❧ The Perilous Journey ❧

THE MIST HAD BARELY CLEARED FROM BETSEY'S EYES before the carriage stopped in the town square, where they found the Clouston's carriage and wagon waiting for them. Sena, Louise, and Margaret had been ordered to leave for the same reason as the Royces. Betsey knew that her godmother, Sena Clouston, and her two sisters had been passing information to their brothers in the Rebel army. Betsey had to giggle when she thought about the Clouston brothers being in her father's company and having to salute him as their captain. Before the war, they were all just good friends.

The Cloustons had friends in Columbia and planned to stay there as long as possible. They had several wagons filled with things from their house, including a grand piano. The little group of carriages gathered together in the square were surrounded by townspeople wanting to say good-bye to their first refugees.

Although both families were leaving homes they might never see again and faced an uncertain future, their friends made it as pleasant as possible. The carriages were heaped with spring flowers, and everyone gathered around them, holding their hands and wishing them godspeed.

"This is more like a reception, Martha," Sena Clouston remarked to Betsey's mother.

"Indeed, Sena," Martha replied, "I never knew we had so many friends. I feel as if we were starting on a pleasure trip." But she couldn't help ending with a deep sigh.

Just then, Mr. McNutt pushed his way through the crowd. "Good-bye, ma'am," he said, choking a little as he tried to smile. "It won't be long till we have you all back again. I'll take good care of the books and portraits, and Alice will look after Charlie Cat."

At the mention of Charlie Cat's name, Sally's lips trembled. Betsey quickly gave her a hug.

"You've been very, very kind, dear Mr. McNutt," Martha replied with a voice close to tears. "And I shall always remember it. I hope you are right about a speedy return, but I feel it is most uncertain. Everything is uncertain now," she said sadly. They shook hands warmly and parted.

At last the order was given, and the little procession started on its way, with a Yankee officer and a guard of mounted soldiers at their side. Betsey felt good and bad when she heard all their Franklin friends calling out to them as they left the square. It was good to know they had so many friends, but bad because she didn't know when, or if, they would see them again.

They moved slowly along Columbia turnpike, passed the first and second picket posts, and then stopped. The officer rode up to the carriages.

"You are now beyond our lines, ladies. I will bid you farewell and wish you a pleasant trip." The ladies bowed silently. Martha turned to him and held out the key to her house.

"I will give this to you for safe keeping," she said, "and hope that you will see that my house is not destroyed."

"Doesn't it seem funny not to see any soldiers around?" Betsey commented as they resumed travel. "We seem so little and lost going on by ourselves."

"We can do without their company very nicely," Martha said. "I, for one, will not miss them."

"Oh, look," said Sally, "the Cloustons are stopping. I wonder why?"

Sena Clouston wanted to visit with her dear friend, Martha Royce, so she asked Betsey and Sally to hop down and go ride with her sister, Margaret. Sally had a hard time getting comfortable on a little hassock in the Clouston's buggy, even though it was the right size for her.

"This thing isn't comfortable," whined Sally. "It's humpy."

"Sh-sh-sh!" Margaret looked at Sally sternly and gave her a warning look. After that, Sally only wiggled silently, for she knew there were times when little girls just had to keep quiet.

After Sena had joined Martha on the carriage, she said, "Oh, Martha, it is so good to be with you. I have so much to tell you."

Martha whispered in her ear, "Be careful what you say. Our drivers are Union men and they could turn us in if we act suspiciously.

"Very well," agreed Sena. "The weather is fine and this is a glorious day!"

"I see some soldiers coming," Betsey said in a worried voice.

Sally, who couldn't see because she was behind the dashboard of the buggy, pulled herself up and looked over. As the soldiers got closer, both girls clapped their hands and shouted, "Those coats aren't blue—they're gray!" The carriages were soon surrounded by their own soldiers. The commander greeted them warmly and invited them to General Earl Van Dorn's headquarters.

"It will give us great pleasure to do so," replied Sena, speaking for the rest. "We cannot see enough of the gray uniforms just now."

"You do us honor," said the young man, bowing. "I shall ride back and tell the general of your coming."

Sena remembered the gossip about how handsome the general was—and a bachelor, too. "Oh, Martha, is my hat on straight and do my curls need rearranging?" Martha only smiled.

Before long, they arrived at the camp, where friendly men in uniforms of various colors—some gray, some butternut brown, some a mixture of both—surrounded them, admiring and sympathizing. Each woman was made to feel like a queen.

They were escorted to a house where Van Dorn had his headquarters. The general and his staff came out to meet them and offered them refreshments. Betsy and Sally were disappointed when the only thing their grownups would accept was water. It was served from handsome silver. The beautiful and ornate seemed like the right complement for the dashing Van Dorn. Betsey, who loved beauty of any kind, couldn't keep her eyes from him, as she took in each detail of his face and dress. She noticed the perfection of his gray uniform, with its gold braid and bright buttons. A long gold watch chain hung about his neck.

After a pleasant visit, the carriages were escorted to the road that would take them to Columbia. By nightfall, they were ten miles from home in a small village where they found a place to spend the night.

Once they were settled in their rooms, many secrets were shared. The women talked until very late, while Sally slept and Betsey tried not to! She didn't want to miss anything, especially when she saw five pistols taken from the Clouston's luggage. Martha showed the pieces of her pistol and told the story of its capture.

"I was afraid to bring all of my guns," she explained, "for I was told we would be searched before we left the Yankee lines."

"We didn't hear that, or we would not have been so bold," replied Louise. "Had we been searched we would have lost all five of ours. I wonder why they didn't? But never mind, we forgive them!"

At this point Margaret broke in with a laugh. "Poor little Sally was so uncomfortable riding on the hassock, where we hid two pistols wrapped in a uniform for General Wheeler. I had to be really stern with her to keep her quiet. As she was getting ready for bed," Margaret continued, "I told her what was in the hassock and how she had helped our soldiers by sitting on the 'humpy' hassock. Sally grinned at me, clapped hands, and said 'Oh, Miss Margaret, I'm so glad.'"

The next day, they went on without any problems. When they crossed the Duck River outside of Columbia, Betsey and Sally made each other laugh with talk of a river full of ducks.

For the Cloustons, it was the end of their journey. They had rented a house in Columbia and would stay there until it was safe to return to Franklin. The Royces had been invited to stay with them until the Ramseys arrived. By the end of the week, they were joined by Martha's younger sister, Julia, her husband William Ramsey and their children — two little boys and a baby girl with Patty, her Negro nurse.

Betsey loved her Aunt Julia, who was pretty and fun to be with no matter what they were doing. Uncle William was very serious and could not join the army like other men his age because he had delicate lungs. Betsey thought it was good that Uncle William was there to help them, since the trip to Greeneville would take some serious planning.

William showed the ladies he had given a lot of thought as to how they would go to Greeneville. He explained that since many railroads had been destroyed, they would have to go in a roundabout way.

"We will go forty miles to Shelbyville, where we can connect with a main line to Chattanooga, and then on to Greeneville. If the road to Shelbyville has been destroyed, then we will have to go to Huntsville, Alabama, and from there to Chattanooga and Greeneville."

"What will we travel in to get to Shelbyville?" asked Martha.

"I will hire a carriage and a wagon. The wagon I will drive myself with the older children and the baggage." The plan sounded good, but trying to fit the baggage and the older children in one wagon was impossible. William hired an open spring-wagon filled with straw for the children.

With everyone in place, they gave the Cloustons an affectionate farewell and started the journey to Shelbyville. They plodded slowly onward all that day, stopping now and then to ask directions, get water from a spring, or to spread out their lunch and rest the horses. At first, the children had fun seeing new things as they rode along, but after a while they grew tired and hot as the sun beat down on their uncovered wagon. The countryside grew more and more hilly, the distance between houses longer. As evening came on, the sky covered with dark clouds and the rumble of thunder was heard more often.

"I wonder when we are going to stop for the night," Martha said to her sister. "It has been three miles since we passed a house and the sun is setting."

"I know," Julia replied uneasily, "and I also think a storm is coming. I'm scared to death of lightning. I wish we would see a house." Hugging her baby closer, she peered out through the darkness. Martha said nothing, but tried to urge on the tired horse. The road seemed to grow rougher and more hilly as the darkness became black as ink, broken by blinding flashes of lightning. Crashes of thunder went echoing among the hills.

At a sudden shout from William, Martha pulled up her horse just as a vivid flash showed her that William had missed the road and that his horse had fallen in a heap. Luckily, the horse was not hurt, and with a little urging was soon on his feet and moving again. Holding on to each other, the children huddled together, too frightened to make any noise.

"This won't do," said Martha, after driving on a short distance. "I can't see the road, and pretty soon our horse will be down just like William's was, and maybe too crippled to go on." Speaking to the Negro maid, she said, "Patty, you must get out and walk ahead in the road. I will follow your white head kerchief as I drive. Julia, you will have to take the baby. Never mind about the lightning—we all have to die sometime."

The change was made and Patty stumbled on in front, her headgear guiding like a white beacon, while Julia shrieked each time a bolt of lightning lit up the sky.

Then it began to rain, at first only a few splashes, then harder and harder until, at last, the heavens opened and torrents fell.

"The children will be soaked," cried Julia. "There's not a bit of shelter on their wagon."

"The rain is warm and won't chill them, and their clothes can be dried," Martha replied. "But how I wish we could see a house."

Just then Patty called back, "Miz Julia, I sees a light." At the same time, William confirmed the happy news. With great relief they urged the exhausted horses through the pelting rain until they finally reached a lighted log cabin.

The cabin was not very attractive, but everyone was so anxious for shelter that they didn't mind what it looked like, as long as it had a roof.

"We'll sit here while William goes up and asks," said Julia, "The children are already as wet as can be. He's going up to the door now." In a moment they could hear William gently inquiring and a woman's shrill, angry reply.

"It doesn't look good. I think I'd better see if I can help him," said Martha. And with that she jumped out and ran through the rain to the house.

By this time, the woman had planted herself in the doorway so no one could get by her. "My house is packed full of soldiers," she said, "and I won't take in another soul."

"But," Martha said, "we are women and children out in the storm, and one is a little baby. Maybe you are a mother yourself?"

"H'it ain't any of your damned business what I am," the

THE PERILOUS JOURNEY

BY THIS TIME THE WOMAN HAD PLANTED
HERSELF IN THE DOORWAY
SO NO ONE COULD GET BY HER.
"MY HOUSE IS PACKED FULL OF SOLDIERS,"
SHE SAID, "AND I WON'T TAKE IN ANOTHER SOUL!"

woman shrieked. "I tell you, I won't have any of you in my house and you can just go on."

"Hello, what's this all about?" cried a man's voice as a door swung open and a man in gray walked out, followed by others in like dress. "What?" he exclaimed, taking in the situation, "You'll let women and children stay out in the storm and won't give them shelter? Woman, what are you made of?"

Then, looking at Martha, he said, "Y'all come straight in and take this room. Me and my men will go to the barn. That's plenty good enough for us."

And brushing aside the angry woman barring the door, the soldiers poured out into the rain. A short time later, the wet and weary travelers were settled in the big warm room that the soldiers had given up for them.

"I am sooooo glad to get out of my soppy wet dress," Betsey said to Sally as they got ready for bed. No sooner had they pulled the blanket up than they were sound asleep.

The next day was beautiful, sunny and warm. It was hard to believe they had been so cold and wet the night before.

William Ramsey learned from the soldiers that it was useless to go to Shelbyville. The road had been destroyed. So they changed direction and headed south to Huntsville, Alabama. The horses were tired, the roads poor. The sun got hotter and their progress slower.

"How long before we get to Greeneville, Mother?" asked Sally. "I'm getting awfully tired of sitting in the wagon. It's not much better than my humpy hassock in the buggy."

"Sally," replied her mother, "you must learn to be patient. We have a long way to go. No one knows how many days it will take us to reach Greeneville. You and Betsey will have to make up games to play along the way."

Betsey remembered how she had promised her father to take care of Sally and help her mother while he was gone. But this was turning out to be more of a job than she thought it would be.

"All right, Sally," she said, "we're going to play as many games as we can think of, and then we can make up some new ones. When we're tired of playing games, we can sing. Singing always makes us feel good."

After a lot of games and much singing, the carriages and

wagons finally pulled into Huntsville. It took them four days, but it seemed like four weeks. With a sigh of relief, the Ramseys and Royces boarded the train to Chattanooga. Seats on the train were not much better than the wagons and carriages, but knowing they were finally moving toward Greeneville made it easier to be patient.

But as night came on, they still hadn't reached Chattanooga. The train seemed to go slower, as if feeling its way through the night. One by one, the weary passengers dropped off to sleep as best they could.

"How long till we reach Chattanooga, William?" Julia asked her husband. She was very tired, and even the good little baby had begun to cry and fuss.

"We should be there by this time," he answered, "but the train is late.

"However," he added, looking at his watch, "I think we should be there in another hour." But it was much later when the train crawled to a stop at the Chattanooga station.

"Chattanooga! Change for Knoxville!" shouted the conductor. The unhappy passengers gathered up their luggage and sleepy children and stepped onto the dirty and badly lit platform.

"Stand here for a moment," William directed, "until I can find out when our train leaves." He was back shortly with news that the train to Knoxville did not leave until three thirty in the morning. "There is a hotel nearby where we can wait. Stay here while I see to our baggage."

The women and children huddled together in the dim light as they watched some groups of passing soldiers. What was more frightening, they also saw a group of men who slouched in the shadows and seemed to have no good reason to be there.

"This is really an evil-looking spot," Martha remarked to Julia. "I shall be glad when we're out of it!"

"So shall I!" Julia agreed. "Oh, will we ever see home?"

William returned and reported that the baggage was all there, but had to stay on the platform since it could not be locked up.

"I hope it will be all right," he said with concern.

Martha was instantly wide awake, "William, it won't be all right. Just look around and see the kind of men who are prowling about. Everything will be stolen by the time we leave if it isn't locked up. Let's go back to the agent and see what we can do."

The agent was of little help. He refused to lock up the baggage. But he did offer to find someone they could hire to guard it until their train left. Since they had no other choice, a "guard" was hired to watch their things.

"That man doesn't look very trustworthy," William commented as they walked away together, "but I don't see that we can help ourselves."

"I wouldn't trust him with five cents," agreed Martha. "We can only hope for the best."

The time they spent waiting at the hotel was an experience they never wanted to talk about. Their rooms were dirty and without locks on the doors. Martha and the Ramseys took turns closing their eyes while the children slept.

Shortly after three o'clock in the morning, they gladly left the squalid hotel. Shivering, they crossed the dark street and entered the dismal station for the final part of the long trip to Greeneville. After the children and Julia were settled on the train, Martha and William went to count their baggage. Two out of three belonging to the Royces were missing. At once they turned to the guard, who, dazed and confused, started to mumble something.

"Come along with me to the agent," Martha ordered sternly. "I am going to report you." William took the man by the arm as he stumbled along, still mumbling. The report was made, but the agent only nodded and said he was sorry. Just then, the train whistle blew.

"No use, Martha," said William, "Come on, the train is starting." As they hurried along, he continued, "We have fallen into a gang of thieves. But you can advertise as soon as we reach home. Perhaps you can recover something."

"I had three trunks, which was all I could take from our home," sighed Martha. "And now I have only one!"

Betsey and Sally looked at their mother in disbelief when she told them what had happened.

"Oh, Mother!" Sally cried. "I'm afraid they have taken Rose and Belle!" And the tears began to trickle down her cheeks.

Betsey didn't mind the possible loss of the dolls too much, since she hadn't played with them for some time. But she was so tired of all that had gone wrong since leaving Franklin, and the loss of the trunks was too much. She wiped away many tears with her long curls before her head nodded forward and she fell asleep.

The next morning, their train pulled into the Greeneville station, and the weary travelers stepped down onto the platform. Their spirits rose when they saw the family carriage and a spring wagon waiting for them, along with a wagon for the baggage.

"There is Charles with the carriage," Julia exclaimed. "And Jesse with the spring wagon for the children. And I do believe that is Bob with the other wagon. How he has grown." Joyfully, the sisters went to speak to the men, who greeted them with cheerful grins and many a "Howdy, Miss Martha!" and "Howdy, Miss Julia!" and "Ol' Missus will shorely be glad to see dese chillun."

Once everyone was seated, they started the five-mile drive to the old homestead. Almost before Betsey knew it, she saw her grandparents' home in the distance. A few moments later, they were in the driveway, and from all directions people came running to welcome them. The long hard trip was over, and the mansion opened wide its hospitable doors and offered rest and shelter to nine weary travelers.

Chapter Five
❧ Back At The Old Home ❧

BETSEY AND SALLY COULD HARDLY BELIEVE how beautiful and peaceful life was at their grandparents' home compared with the last days in Franklin and the terrible trip from Columbia to Greeneville.

To them, Walnut Hill, as the plantation was called, was a paradise of never-ending delights. Its broad and fertile acres lay in the wide bowl of the Nolichucky River, against the background of the Great Smoky Mountains. The hazy ridges stretched as far away as the eye could see. The mansion itself, wide and spacious, stood on a hill shaded by the noble trees that gave it its name. Behind the house, at convenient distances, stood the kitchen, loom-house, smoke house, ice house, corn house, and doctor's office. Beyond that were several houses making up the slave quarters; and, finally, the big, wide-roofed barn. Along the foot of the hill ran a brook, close by a near press (see Appendix), a smithy, spring house/dairy and a grist mill for the use of the place.

Tall trees, choice shrubbery, and stately boxwood-bordered walks surrounded the house, but the flower garden that lay to the right of it was the delight and pastime of Betsey's Grandmother Broyles. The paths wound in and out in the intricate "Italian

Pattern," surrounding beds of bloom and fragrance. Beyond were plantings of fruit and vine. Orchards spread themselves on sunny slopes, and sheep and cattle grazed in grassy meadows. Within their designated areas were turkeys, geese, and chickens. Nearby, proud peacocks strutted majestically. From two large apiaries, bees buzzed in ceaseless activity, and great stores of honey were laid by for winter use.

All in all, Walnut Hill was a well-functioning example of the antebellum "Southern way of life." Few realized that way of life would soon be in its death throes!

Betsey not only loved her grandparents, she respected them. She knew her grandfather expected the best, not only from her, but from everyone at Walnut Hill. He was a man of strong moral character, which was reflected in his treatment of bond servants. No slave went poorly fed, poorly clothed, or poorly housed. Each married man among them had his own little house and garden, and sometimes a few chickens or a hive or two of bees. They could sell extra honey and chickens for some money of their own.

Dr. Broyles was a doctor with a large country practice, and was often called away from home. As a result, he once tried having an overseer, but the man was told to leave when it was discovered how harshly he was treating the slaves.

Betsey's grandmother had more to do than anyone at Walnut Hill. She started her day while it was still dark. No activity on the plantation went without her supervision. She began by distributing food supplies to the cook and individual slave families. Then she went to the dairy, where she turned the cheese press or prepared curd for fresh cheese. The loom house she directed with special care, for it produced the cloth which not only clothed the slaves, but also furnished much of the family's clothes, plus table linen, toweling, carpets, blankets, and yarn for stockings, both wool and cotton. Flax and wool were produced at Walnut Hill, and every year a bale of cotton came to Grandmother Broyles from her family's plantation in South Carolina. All this raw material had to be converted into finished products under her watchful eye. It was no wonder her day started so early.

Grandmother Broyles set up the warp of every piece of cloth that went into the loom, whether white, solid color, or a combination of color in stripes or checks. Betsey loved watching her grandmother dip hanks of yarn in big dye pots and then test the color. In the loom house, Betsey was taught to whirl the big wheel, which clicked delightfully as it marked the "cuts." Sometimes she would just stand and watch, fascinated as the black woman weaving at the loom sent the shuttle flying back and forth.

There were other interesting things for Betsey to watch, such as making candles. They were run in molds after Grandmother Broyles had carefully adjusted the wicks. These special candles were for use in the big crystal chandelier with its glistening prisms, and were only lit for grand occasions.

Often Betsey would follow her grandmother down to the spring house, another special place with its cool stone floor, through which water flowed from the deep blue spring outside. There she would watch while Grandmother Broyles instructed Rindy, the dairy woman, as to the best method for skimming the yellow cream or churning the fragrant butter. And Betsey was always glad when her grandmother's steps turned toward the river, where amid steam from the boiling pots, Polly stood under a shed on the bank and scrubbed the family linen. Then she rinsed it in the river, standing in a boat which was tied to a tree.

Soon after their arrival, Martha gave the children their first lesson in the etiquette of the plantation.

"When you speak to the older Negroes," she began, "you must call them 'Uncle' and 'Aunt.'

"But, why?" asked Betsey, "They are not really our aunts and uncles, like Aunt Julia and Uncle William."

"Of course not," Martha replied, "we call them so only to show respect to their age."

"Mother," Sally piped up, "are Negroes always black?"

"Yes, certainly," Martha answered, caught off her guard, "They are always black, just as we are always white."

"Then why is Charles so white?" Sally asked with a puzzled look. Charles was the coachman, one of the slaves Grandmother Broyles had inherited from her father's plantation in South Carolina.

"Yes," Betsey chimed in, "and Esther is nearly as white." Esther was Charles' sister.

"Never mind about Charles or Esther," their mother answered with heightened color in her cheeks. "Sometimes Negroes are not quite all black and little girls must not ask questions about them!" Betsey and Sally left their mother alone and went off to play.

There were more things to do and think about than skin color.

Martha had an unexpected surprise when her stolen trunks were returned to her. They were found along the railroad tracks, partially opened. Only a few things were missing, one of which was a favorite blue dress and matching bonnet.

"I know I should be happy that the trunks were returned, but I'm going to miss my blue dress, and I worked so hard decorating the bonnet to go with it," Martha said sadly.

The best part of having the trunks returned was having Rose and Belle back in the arms of their delighted little mothers.

In June came the happy day when little Aunt Georgia Broyles returned home from boarding school. The youngest of the family, she was fourteen and full of fun, with auburn hair floating over her shoulders. Betsey loved being with her, as Georgia could always think of great things to do.

For instance, it was fun to see how many children they could pile on a horse before they fell off (the record was five). They went into the hayfields and watched the towering loads slowly moving off, or sat on a wooded slope and saw the reapers cut their rhythmic way across the golden fields of wheat.

Each year, at the end of the harvest, it was Dr. Broyles' custom to give a feast for his slaves. Long tables were spread under the trees on the lawn and the slaves were treated to all kinds of good things. On that day, the usual order of their lives was reversed, with the mistress and her daughters coming out to pass the food and wait on their slaves.

In those golden days of peace and prosperity, Betsey forgot that she had ever heard the singing of the Minies, or looked on the dead and dying, or faced the terror of the dark night when her hands had clasped the cold steel of the carbine. She sometimes thought of her father and wondered where he was, but gradually her memory of him grew dim.

One day in late summer they were reminded that a war was

still going on. Far off and faint, when the wind was in the right direction, they heard the distinct booming of a cannon. It was easy not to listen for it when there was so much happening at Walnut Hill. Betsey hoped they could always stay there and that the cannons would never get any louder.

Grandmother Broyles surprised Betsey when she came from the loom house with a roll of gray cotton homespun in her arms. She said to Martha, "I've just taken this off the loom and I want to give you enough for Betsey and Sally to each have a new dress. This will outwear two of store material."

"You had better have some shoes made for them as well," Grandmother Broyles went on. "Theirs are worn out and grown out, too. Some hides have just come back from the tannery, so I think there is enough for all three of you." What a relief for Martha, since shoes were one thing she could not make.

Betsey had never had a chance to pick out her own material for new dresses. She had to take what was given to her. Very often it was one of her mother's dresses cut down to fit her. Now Grandmother Broyles was holding up a brown plaid dress that used to be Georgia's. Betsey knew Georgia never liked it, and now she would have to wear it! She knew better than to complain. Clothes were scarce, and they were lucky to have ones that didn't have a lot of patches on them.

Late in August, a letter came to Martha, addressed in Moses' beautiful and distinctive handwriting. It had never been sealed and had postmarks of Nashville, Washington and Richmond. With a sinking heart, Martha carried it up to her room before she read it. She felt better the more she read, for although he was a prisoner of war, Moses was well and comfortable. He hoped it

BACK AT THE OLD HOME

FROM THE SMOKEHOUSE, WHICH STOOD WIDE
OPEN, A STREAM OF SOLDIERS POURED OUT,
CARRYING OFF ITS CONTENTS.

wouldn't be long before he was exchanged or paroled.

When Martha explained this to the girls, they were upset at first, but felt better when they understood that their father was out of harm's way. Later, when strangers asked them where their father was, they said, "Father is in jail."

On a day early in September, Betsey sat upstairs reading. She happened to gaze out the window and couldn't believe what she was seeing. A company of Yankees with many big army wagons was heading up the lane toward the barn! Her heart beating furiously, she stared in dumb astonishment as the familiar grounds filled with blue coats. They were a foraging party, intent upon stripping Walnut Hill of its abundance as fast as they could.

Betsey hurried downstairs and looked with horror at what seemed to be the destruction of her little paradise. She saw her grandfather walking here and there, out to the barn, over to the smokehouse, as if his presence would stop the "blue tide." Betsey watched as wagon after wagon drove away from the barn, piled high with hay and fodder. From the smokehouse, which stood wide open, a stream of soldiers poured out, carrying off its contents. Chickens squawked with fright as they were gathered up and carried away in flapping bunches.

Dr. Broyles watched in despair as his stables were rapidly emptied of all the horses and mules. He felt a real heartache as he spotted the graceful outlines of his own and his daughter's saddle horses, prancing down the lane, led by the soldiers.

Hungry men grabbed the dinner right off the stove, ignoring

the cook's protest, and leaving the family to such cold leftovers as they could find. Everywhere the slaves ran about, doing whatever the soldiers wanted, or just stood gaping at the turmoil, while in their minds new thoughts struggled to be born.

Erect and stern, Mrs. Broyles stood by the storehouse which she was forced to open, watching two slave women fill the soldiers' canteens with molasses. Everything in the storehouse had been carried away but the molasses, which will not be hurried, even for an army.

Martha, watching from the window, saw her mother standing by the storehouse with soldiers all around her. "I don't think we should leave our mother all alone out there," she said to her sisters. The others agreed and they were soon at their mother's side.

"Girls!" Mrs. Broyles scolded, "why are you coming out here? This is no place for you. It doesn't matter for an old woman like me who can very well hold her own; but you young women have no business among all these soldiers. I won't allow it. Now go back to the house, straight to your rooms and stay there!"

Although the two daughters so sternly spoken to were mothers themselves, it never occurred to them to question their mother's will. With one accord, they turned back to the house.

"One moment, Georgia," her mother said, calling her back. "Go with your sister Martha to her room and on no account let her come down, no matter what happens." The child nodded and ran back. Mrs. Broyles feared more for her oldest daughter than the rest, knowing how fearless was her spirit when aroused.

As directed, the daughters went at once to their separate rooms, where they watched from their windows the looting of their home. With Martha were Betsey, Sally, and the vigilant Georgia. But none of them talked much, all straining their ears for sounds from the storm outside. Suddenly there came a loud outcry and a shout from somewhere below. Martha rushed towards the door.

"Don't go down, sister Martha. Don't! Don't," cried Georgia, clinging to her. Sally clutched her skirts and Betsey held onto her mother's arm. Georgia managed to turn the key in the lock and slip the key into her pocket. Then she stationed herself in front of the door, a look of determination on her little face. At such a time, she lived up to her fiery red hair.

Martha dropped into a chair and began to laugh. Since no further sounds reached them, she decided to remain where she was. "You hold the key to the situation, don't you, Georgia?" she teased her spirited little sister.

"Mother told me not to let you out," Georgia replied. She looked out the window and added, "I think they must be leaving, for no more wagons are coming and I don't see so many soldiers. There go two of Father's men, Mose and Willis, with the soldiers. They are leading four of our mules. Why do you suppose they are going, sister Martha?"

"They are going because they think they will be free when they reach the Union troops," Martha answered. "It wouldn't surprise me if they all left."

"But, sister, you don't mean that Esther would go, or Hannah, or Polly?" Georgia exclaimed, horrified at the possibility. "We have always treated them so kindly and they have been here all their lives." The tears rose in her eyes.

"They may not go now," replied the older sister, "but in the end..." She paused as though trying to see into the future. "...in the end they will."

As fast as the Yankee foraging party had come, they were gone, leaving those at Walnut Hill to make do with what they left behind. It was good that the corn crop had not yet been gathered, nor the late apples and potatoes. A fair number of cattle and hogs had escaped and, together with most of the poultry, had successfully found shelter during the invasion. Gradually the storehouse would be refilled.

In time, the victims of war got back on their feet. The raid was a warning, however, that they needed to prepare themselves for future trouble that was sure to follow. A "council of war" was held behind closed doors to discuss a course of action.

"We can't hide the land or the slaves," said Dr. Broyles, "so it is only a question of securing the silver and jewels and other small personal belongings which we value."

After much discussion, it was decided to bury the silver in a box which would be taken to a barn farthest from the house. When the box was filled, Dr. Broyles and William Ramsey waited until late at night for their trip to the remote barn. There, by the light of a lantern, the box was buried under a shed to protect it from the weather. Had they looked up, they might have seen the glistening black eyes of one of Dr. Broyles' slaves, eagerly watching them from the hayloft where he lay hiding. Once the men had gone, the box was dug up, and the contents sold to a silversmith in Knoxville.

The largest piece in the box was a coffee urn which the thieves decided was too heavy and cumbersome to carry, and might be identified with Walnut Hill. Anxious to be rid of it, they threw it into some thick bushes nearby. (To find out what eventually happened to this urn, see the Appendix).

Late one night, not long after this, Martha Royce and her father slipped quietly out of the house, down the hill, and across the brook, into the woods beyond. There, in a spot so protected by a large rock and tree as to make it impossible to pitch a tent or build a campfire, they dug a hole without a light to guide them. There they buried her own little treasures in a sealed tin box. (One of Betsey's most valued possessions in later years was a small silver cup which had been buried there for two years.)

The October days had begun to grow nippy, and one night the family was sitting in a wide circle in the cheerful light from the fireplace when Esther appeared at the door.

"Master," she announced, "Mose and Willis have done come back."

"Tell them to come in here," Dr. Broyles replied, "I want to see them." And in a few moments the two young men who had gone away with the Union troops were ushered in. With downcast eyes, they stood before the master, clutching their hats in their hands. Their clothes were worn, their faces distraught.

"Well, boys," Dr. Broyles addressed them in his grave but kindly voice, "what made you decide to come back to me? I thought I would never see you again."

The renegades exchanged looks; then Mose spoke: "Da cap'n, he say 'We ain't got no use for no more slaves here; dere's too many already, and we hain't food enuf for all. You go long back to your marssa and stay dere till we wants you.'"

At this point, Willis took up the story: "And while we was dere, dey worked us in the trenches and sometimes cussed us, and we slept outdoors and was cold and most all de time we was hungry, and, to tell de truth, we's hungry now," he concluded, beginning to blubber.

"But what do you want me to do?" asked Dr. Broyles.

"We wants to ax yore pardon, marster," replied Mose. "And we wants you to take us back, and we don't want to run away no more."

"Very well, boys," returned the master, "I'll take you back this time, but see that you don't run off again. You may begin work in the potato field tomorrow; but just now go out in the kitchen and tell Hannah to give you your supper."

After that, there were no more runaways. All the slaves remained on the place until the war ended and they knew they were free. Then their new sense of liberty proved stronger than their personal loyalties to former owners, and they pooled up their small belongings and, one by one, all departed.

Through the cold months of 1863–64, the family was surrounded by friends, for General James Longstreet wintered in East Tennessee. Kershaw's division was stationed near Greeneville. A gallant band of tall and vigorous Broyles cousins from South Carolina made the mansion at Walnut Hill lively with their presence as they came and went. In all the nine years of her life, Betsey had never dreamed that life could be so merry as it was that winter. The house was always full to capacity, the dining table in constant use with talk of army life and adventures. In the evening, the parlor overflowed with singing and dancing. Betsey would listen and look from a corner of the room until she was spotted by her mother. As she went reluctantly up the long stairs to her room, the joyful sounds would follow her, and with each step she would murmur, "I wish I was grown up. Oh, I wish I was grown up."

Everyone at these gatherings sang, with no concern if they were in tune. They sang simple melodies as well as part songs. War songs held the first place, full of the spirit of battle or expressing the sorrow and longing of those left behind. Songs of love were always popular, though often sad. Much as Betsey loved songs which made her delightfully unhappy, she sometimes wondered why so many people died and were laid away under weeping willows, with daisies waving over them.

Christmas was full of joy and good spirits, which made up for the scarcity of even homemade gifts. There was no peace on earth, and good will to men prevailed only in certain limited sections. But Walnut Hill made very merry.

"Martha," said Mrs. Broyles, "I understand that you are a master hand with eggnog. Won't you make it for me? I want to go out to the kitchen and show Hannah a new dressing for the turkey."

"Of course, Mother," replied Martha, "I'll make it with pleasure."

"I'll be greatly obliged," returned Mrs. Broyles. "Here are the keys to the spirits, and Esther will bring you what else you need. You may work at the side table in the dining room." And she went out to the kitchen.

Humming "Maryland, My Maryland" under her breath, Martha applied herself gaily to mixing and beating. She was nearing the end of her pleasant task when Esther came in and handed her a letter.

"A man has just brought it, Miss Martha," she said. A glance showed Martha her husband's handwriting, and her song died away as she tore the envelope open.

Arriving a moment later, Betsey saw her mother drop heavily into a chair, her face white to the lips, and in her hand a letter and a photograph.

"Betsey," Martha whispered in a distant voice, "your father has been sentenced to die!"

Chapter Six
❦ The Shadow Of Death ❦

THE LETTER THAT HAD SO STRICKEN MARTHA read as follows:

Military Prison
Nashville, Tenn.
December 18, 1863

Dear Wife:

I have been tried on a charge of guerilla warfare, have been adjudged guilty, and am now under sentence to be shot. The date of my execution has not been fixed.

It is needless to tell you that I am innocent of the charge. I have only been a scout. I enclose a photograph of myself, which I was allowed to have taken, attended by a guard. You are not likely to forget my looks, but the children would.

May the Lord have you in his keeping. Farewell.

Faithfully your husband,

Moses Royce

Within a moment, Martha's family had gathered around her, offering words of comfort and encouragement until, gradually, the color came back to her face. Turning over the letter, she looked at the date.

"It is just a week since this was written," she remarked, shuddering. "Much may have happened since then."

As the spirit of battle dawned in her eyes, she looked up at her father, who stood nearby, and rose unsteadily to her feet.

"Come with me, Father," she said, laying her hand on his arm. "I want to talk with you privately." And together they went off to another part of the house.

"Martha, my child," he said as they sat down, "this is indeed a terrible blow. But you must face it bravely and not give up hope. Remember, Moses has influential relatives in New England who will leave no stone unturned to save his life. He is doubtless in communication with them through his mother—and he is her only son."

"That is quite possible, Father," replied Martha. "But I still feel that no time must be lost. I am going at once to Richmond to see President Davis and prevail upon him to intervene on my husband's behalf. If the Yankees refuse to exchange him, then to hold some prominent Union prisoner as hostage for his safety."

Her eyes sparkled. "Father!" she cried, springing to her feet, "are any of the men of Andy Johnson's family at their home in Greeneville now?" (Andrew Johnson was the military governor of Tennessee and a future senator, vice president of the United States, and the president who succeeded Abraham Lincoln after Lincoln was assassinated.)

Her father looked at her in astonishment. "Martha!" he

exclaimed as he stood to face her. "It isn't possible. You wouldn't dream of doing such a thing."

The blue steel of Martha's eyes met his. "Father," she answered quietly, "if any one of them are at home, he will be seized and held for my husband within twenty-four hours. Our army is here, and I have many friends among them."

"I am quite sure that none of Governor Johnson's family is presently in Greeneville, Martha. They are probably in Nashville," replied her father, obviously relieved that such was the case. "But if you must go to Richmond," he went on, glad to lead the talk in another direction, "that would be a most difficult and dangerous journey for you—impossible, I should say, for a woman alone. I am too old to go with you and am needed at home; and William is hardly strong enough for such a journey in winter."

"I don't believe I could go alone," Martha replied, "but I think John Morris would go with me. He probably could get a leave of absence if the circumstances were known; and I'm sure he would do anything for me." (John Morris was a young cousin, then stationed with General Joseph Kershaw.)

"That sounds like a good plan," her father said. With an escort decided upon, they went on to discuss ways and means for her departure in two days.

On the day before she was to leave, Martha sat down to have a quiet talk with her children. They were both very attentive as they looked at their mother. This would be the first time they were separated.

"You know why I am going away," she told them as they sat beside her, their young faces very serious. "Your father's life is at stake and I must do all in my power to save him. You are to stay with Grandmother, who will take good care of you. You both must be obedient and give no trouble. I will return as quickly as I can. Here is the picture your father sent; you may keep it while I am away. Whenever you look at it, remember to pray for his freedom."

In silence, Betsey took the picture from her mother's hand and sat looking up at her. The tears began to trickle down Sally's plump cheeks.

Looking at her two little girls with such sad expressions, Martha thought of all they had suffered. She knew she must lift their spirits before she could leave them.

"Now you must tell me what you would like me to bring you from Richmond. What would you like, Betsey?"

"I would like a new book," Betsey said. "I have read the old ones so many times I know them by heart."

"Very well, I shall bring you one," replied her mother. "And now, what does Sally want?"

"I want another Charlie Cat more than anything," cried Sally, clasping her hands. A joyful smile spread over her face.

"I think I can manage that easily enough," her mother agreed, patting her head. Then she went to the closet and opened a large box. "Here are two fine cakes I made for Christmas—a pound cake and a fruit cake. I shall turn them over to you, but you may invite Georgia to share them with you."

"Yes, Mother, we will," Betsey replied in her most responsible tone. "And I will see that Sally doesn't eat more than one slice a day."

"Also watch Betsey carefully," Martha teased. With that, the dark cloud lifted and the little girls were smiling while they helped their mother pack.

John Morris' leave of absence began on December 27, and on that day, he and Martha left for Richmond, followed by good wishes and blessings from her family.

Once their mother was out of sight, the happy feelings of the day before vanished. As long as daylight lasted it was not so bad, since they could be outdoors playing. But days were short and nighttime was much harder.

Betsey thought it was better for Sally because she was seven and went to bed early. When her mother was home, Betsey loved staying up later to read and talk. It was special having her mother all to herself. Now it just made her feel worse. Instead of staying with the cheerful group around the fire, she would go to her room to be by herself.

Thoughts of home in Franklin—her little crabapple tree and her father leading their friends in prayers and singing at St. Paul's—would help her feel better. She remembered how she used to talk to her grandmother's portrait and how Grandmother Royce always smiled at her. It wasn't the same when she tried it with her father's picture because he looked so sad and serious.

Then one night Betsey remembered something wonderful about her father that she had almost forgotten. His full name was Moses Strong Royce. She just knew in her heart he was *strong* and he would be alright, and so would her mother.

It was still hard to wait when three weeks passed with no word from her mother. Dr. Broyles tried to explain to the girls that this was not unusual in times of war.

Then, all of a sudden, she was back, to the intense joy of everyone at Walnut Hill, most especially her two little girls! Her parents and family flocked around her, the children beside themselves with relieved happiness. They threw themselves upon her. Looking tired and worn, but radiant, she clung first to one and then another.

At last Sally's little piping voice cut through a storm of questions. "Mother? Did you bring me Charlie Cat?"

"Here he is," she replied as she picked up a small covered basket and handed it to Sally. "He is pure white except for his tail, which is black, and he has two black spots on his head." Sally carried him off with a big smile.

Then, out from her red carpetbag, she drew Betsey's promised books—Bonner's *A Child's History of Rome* in two volumes bound in red like the favorite Abbots. But her crowning surprise for both little girls was a pair of tiny gold earrings. She had promised them earrings the previous summer when they had their ears pierced. These new ones became their pride and delight—their dearest treasure.

After Sally had gone to bed with Charlie Cat by her side, Betsey sat down with her mother for their long-awaited special time together. "I am so glad you are home, Mother. I was worried I might never see you again. Why did it take such a long time to go to Richmond?"

Martha smiled at Betsey and pulled her closer. "First of all, it is a very long way—nearly 330 miles, as best we could estimate. But mostly it took me longer for two big reasons: winter and war.

"Winter made it hard because when we got to Mr. DeVault's

THE SHADOW OF DEATH

"THERE WERE GIANT BLOCKS OF ICE IN THE RIVER,
AND IF ONE HIT US, OUR BOAT WOULD SINK! THREE
MEN IN THE BOAT WITH ME HAD LONG POLES TO
KEEP THE ICE CHUNKS AWAY FROM US."

house on the Watauga River, it was so cold that when I put water on my hair to comb it, it froze!"

"Oh," said Betsey, "that sounds awful."

"Mr. DeVault thought we could cross the river by boat if we used great care," Martha continued. "There were giant blocks of ice in the river and if one hit us, our boat would sink! Three men in the boat with me had long poles to keep the ice chunks away from us."

"I'm very glad the men with the long poles kept the ice away," exclaimed Betsey. "Were you very close to Richmond after you crossed the river?"

"No, I'm afraid not," said Martha. "We still had another river to cross. It was the Holston, and it was even more dangerous because of what the war had done to it."

"I don't understand, Mother..."

"The bridge was burned by the soldiers, Betsey, and the only way left to cross the river was to climb over the blackened timbers which had fallen and lay helter-skelter in the water. The train to Richmond was somewhere on the other side, and if we could only cross, most of our troubles would be over. There were plenty of men and soldiers around. They were looking for the body of a man who had recently drowned trying to cross the river.

"We stood for a while, watching some soldiers who were making their dangerous way across the timbers. I decided to go and not think any longer."

"But, Mother, weren't you awfully scared? I would have been," Betsey said.

"Sometimes, Betsey, it is better to just go ahead and do it. You can't allow your fears to get in the way. I had to save your father and that's what kept me going. I also knew in my heart the good Lord was with me and would protect me."

Betsey looked at her mother and thought how much she loved her for being so brave. She gave her mother an extra hug and urged her to continue.

"I started out alone, but a soldier came to my side and said, 'Allow me to go with you. I will give you what help I can. It is too dangerous for soldiers, let alone a woman by herself.' I gratefully accepted his help. We went on slowly together, sometimes climbing over, sometimes under the great blackened, jagged timbers. The rushing water boiled and tumbled through them, covering them in places with an icy spray. Once or twice I slipped, and would have gone under but for the soldier's helping hand. Near the center, where the current was the strongest, some of the beams had been washed away, and a plank had been thrown across. Below it, the water ran as swift as a waterfall. As I went slowly over the plank, holding the soldier's hand, he said 'I expect that poor fellow they are looking for is right under us now.' It was not a cheering remark at such a critical time."

"I bet you were soooo glad to reach the other side and get on the train to Richmond."

"Yes, Betsey, I certainly was, and it was worth it when I got to see President Davis and he promised me that your father's life would be spared."

Betsey clapped her hands and said, "President Davis must be a very kind man. What was he like, Mother?"

"Well, Betsey, the President was dressed in a gray suit and was tall and thin. He looked pale, careworn and not very strong. He seemed to know things which worried him a great deal, but which he, of course, kept to himself. Remember, Betsey, we must always be grateful to President Davis."

"I will be, Mother, I promise. I hope that after you left the President you had an easier time coming home."

"Well, not really, Betsey. I had to cross the Holston River again. This time the broken timbers had been removed and another railroad bridge was being built. It was forty feet high where it spanned the river and was only partly built. A single plank as wide as the length of my foot ran through the center for the workmen to use."

"Mother! That doesn't seem nearly wide enough."

"You're right, Betsey, it wasn't. But it was all we had to make our crossing. There were a lot of soldiers waiting on each shore. They helped to steady the structure by pulling on ropes that were tied to it. It took twenty men on each side pulling against one another to make it steadier. Just as we were about to cross, one poor soldier who had tried to go over came crawling back along the plank and said, 'Don't go out there; you can't stand it.' But we were determined. We started crawling, and when we felt a gust of wind coming, we would stop and brace ourselves for the shock while our frail support rocked back and forth. We finally made it across, as you can plainly see, since I'm here beside you.

"Well, that's quite enough for one night. Time to say your prayers and go to bed."

Betsey kissed her mother and hugged her tight. "I will be glad to say my prayers tonight. I want to thank God for taking care of you and keeping Father alive."

Martha sat on Betsey's bed, waiting while she nodded off to sleep. She stayed for a while, watching her little girls sleep before joining the rest of the family around the cheerful fire.

In answer to her father's question as to what she had been able to accomplish in Richmond, she replied: "I saw President Davis for only a few minutes, but I received the help I needed to save Moses' life. The President assured me that he would communicate at once with the military authorities in Nashville, requesting a suspended sentence. He also promised me that a Union officer would be held for my husband's safety."

"You have done all that you possibly could," her father declared, "and the fact that the sentence has not yet been carried out shows that influences elsewhere are also at work on his behalf. If it had been carried out, we would have had news by this time."

"While we were in Richmond on his behalf, have any of Governor Johnson's family returned yet?" she asked her father with a twinkle of mischief in her eyes.

"Martha, you are a very naughty woman," Dr. Broyles replied, trying not to smile.

The night of February 29, 1864, was wildly stormy. The wind blew furiously; the icy rain descended in torrents, and neither man nor beast stirred except by necessity. Except for one circumstance, that storm would have been forgotten, as had many others equally violent. But for the Royce family this night would be long remembered, for on that night Captain Royce escaped from prison! Storms rarely shelter, but that one did. Under the cover of the violent storm, Moses Royce and three others made their escape, which remained his favorite story for the rest of his life.

Within a week, the joyful news of his escape reached Walnut Hill. Martha and the girls gave heartfelt thanks. "I'm so glad Father is out of jail!" exclaimed Sally.

In early March, it was obvious that General Longstreet would be moving out. Since Union forces were in possession of Knoxville, it seemed probable that after Longstreet's withdrawal the rest of East Tennessee would fall into Yankee hands.

Martha Royce was in conference with her father and relatives in the army regarding her best course of action. She dreaded falling into enemy hands again.

"You have been good and loving to us, Father," she told him affectionately, "and the old home has been a true haven. But I fear the time is coming when there will be neither safety nor shelter for anyone. Knowing what the children and I have suffered already, I want to stay out of the Yankees' path. I would like to find some protected spot where I could live in safety and where Moses could join us. I have written to friends near Nashville to try to find out where he is."

Barney Broyles, Martha's cousin and an aide to General Kershaw, spoke up: "You have the right idea, cousin Martha," he said. "It would be best for you to leave East Tennessee. I have a plan. Longstreet will be leaving soon; you can come along with us."

"That is a tempting idea," Martha responded, "But what should I do after I go with Longstreet? I cannot enlist."

Barney laughed. "You would make a first rate soldier, Martha, but that isn't my plan. Now listen to what I have in mind: My father, mother and sisters are refugees in Marshallville, not far from Macon, Georgia. Since Marshallville is out of the track of the Union army, at least for the present, I believe you cannot do better than to join my family there."

"But how do I reach that distant spot?" Martha asked. "Travel isn't what it used to be, as I learned when I went to Richmond."

"You don't think I would let you go without an escort!" exclaimed Barney. "I have a month's furlough and will be going down to spend it with my parents after I part company with Longstreet in Virginia. It will give me great pleasure to take you with me."

Martha thought for a few moments. "That sounds entirely practical, cousin," she said. "What do you think, Father?"

"If you must leave—and there is reason enough why you

should—Barney's plan is a good one. You will be safe with your Uncle John and his family. In time, Moses may be able to join you. At any rate, you will be out of the Yankees' reach."

(Dr. Broyles could hardly have been expected to foresee that Marshallville would lay directly in the path of Union General William Tecumseh Sherman's March to the Sea!)

"I shall go with you, Barney," Martha concluded. "How soon do we leave?"

"The orders are expected any day," her cousin answered. "Today is Friday. I would guess we would leave the middle of next week."

"I will be ready," she answered him, thinking that there would be time to have her clothes washed before leaving. *It will be good to have everything clean*, Martha thought.

Monday proved to be a bad wash day. Snow was falling thickly and the clothes froze stiff on the line. But Mrs. Broyles urged Polly to give it her best effort. "Miss Martha is going to travel in a few days," she said, "and she wants to take clean clothes. Be sure you do hers first."

"Yes, missus," responded Polly, "I's done got hers all on de line now. But they's stiff as boards."

Just then, Martha came running out to the wash-house through the snow.

"Mother!" she cried, "Barney is here and the army is moving. I must be ready to go in an hour. He's waiting. The train leaves at two!"

"But your clothes are hanging on the line, frozen," her mother exclaimed. "You can't take them like that."

"I shall have to, Mother," Martha replied. "Here, Polly, help me take them off the line and into the house." The next hour was spent packing the stiff clothes, along with food for the trip.

When the packing was done, the little girls came into the room with their big dolls in their arms. "Mother," Sally pleaded, "don't forget Rose and Belle."

Their mother gave them a hopeless look. The trunks were filled to the top and ready to be closed. "My Dears," she said quietly, "I'm afraid there is no room. You will have to leave them with Georgia. I know she will take the very best care of them. We are going on a long journey, and your dolls might be broken if you tried to carry them." So the children parted with their last toys.

"I 'spect I'd better leave Charlie Cat with Georgia, too," Sally said sadly. Her mother thankfully agreed, while Georgia promised to take very good care of her precious cat.

Everyone exchanged loving but hurried farewells, then Barney helped the family into the carriage. They drove off to the railroad station through whirling snow.

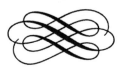

Chapter Seven
❧ Wayfarers Once More ❧

"YOU HAVE BEEN INVITED TO RIDE IN THE OFFICER'S CAR, Cousin Martha," Barney told her.

"I have you to thank, no doubt," replied Martha.

"No, you have General Longstreet to thank. He sent the invitation," Barney said with a smile.

Betsey and Sally quickly made new friends among the officers. Many of them had enjoyed the hospitality of Walnut Hill during the winter.

Slowly they traveled on to Bristol, then to Wytheville in the Virginia mountains. In Wytheville, the frozen clothes were unpacked and dried. After staying two days, they continued the long journey to Marshallville.

The landscape became increasingly flat and uninteresting. In South Carolina and Georgia, the passengers could buy roasted peanuts. There were no eating places along the way, but cooked food was sold at some stations for passengers to carry with them.

Finally, they reached Marshallville where the Royces were welcomed warmly by John Broyles, his wife Claudia, and their two young daughters, Felice and Frances.

"Welcome, Martha; welcome all of you," cried Uncle John as he embraced his niece and her children. "We are just refugees ourselves, camping in a bit of a house until it is safe for us to go back home."

"While Barney is with us, we found a place for you to board with Mrs. Simpson," explained Aunt Claudia. "When Barney's furlough is over we want you with us. You can have the shed room. It isn't much, but we'll be together."

After dinner, Barney escorted Martha and the girls to the end of the street and left them at Mrs. Simpson's gate, saying he would go back and see to their trunks. As they walked up to the house, Betsey was curious about what she saw.

The yard was not large, but was full of tall trees and thick clumps of flowering shrubs, some even bursting into bloom. No grass grew anywhere; only clean, bare, sandy soil could be seen. Built of wood, one story high, the house had never been painted. It stood on high foundation posts. Betsey always called them "legs." The legs kept the house cool and helped air to circulate. The overall effect was not pleasing. Behind the house were many dingy cabins with Negroes of all ages.

Martha went up the steps, but could not knock or ring since there was no door. She saw only an open passageway running straight through the house, with rooms on either side. An untidy Negro girl came towards them. "Jes step in here, ma'am," she said, opening one of the room doors. "Missus will come in a minute."

Feeling more and more forlorn, Martha and the girls entered and sat down in the dark and unkempt room.

"I don't like it here. I want to go back to Grandfather's," cried Sally.

"Quiet, Sally! We are here and we must make the best of it," Martha replied sternly.

WAYFARERS ONCE MORE

As they waited in silence, the door opposite them slowly opened. A young white woman with wild eyes and long disheveled dark hair stuck her head in. She stood a moment with her hand on the door while her distracted eyes focused themselves on the strangers. Uttering a long, wailing cry, she pulled back and closed the door.

Martha sat perfectly still as the little girls turned to her, their eyes full of fear and astonishment. Before they could say a word, the door opened and their landlady entered. Mrs. Simpson was the only ray of comfort the Royces were to find in their unattractive new quarters. A homely, motherly soul, she was uneducated, but kindly and simple. Her methods, however—if they could be called such—were slack and untidy. Her slaves went through their daily routine with such a waste of efficiency that it would have driven Betsey's grandmother to despair. Though sufficiently fed and clothed, they were densely ignorant, dirty, and untrained. Their cabins teemed with children.

The mystery of the strange young woman who first greeted them was explained by Mrs. Simpson. She was a married daughter whose husband was in the Southern army. She had become insane, but because there was no place to send her, they kept her at home. Mrs. Simpson assured them that she was quite harmless.

The Royces devoutly hoped she was, since her room was next to theirs, and the key was on her side of the door.

Once in a while the Simpson daughter would come into their room and go to a chest of drawers where Martha kept her clothes. She pulled the drawers out one by one and rummaged through them rapidly, looking for something she never found. When this happened, Martha and the girls would sit without moving. They did not want to attract her attention. Finally, she would go out quickly, locking the door behind her. At other times, she would beat on the door and sing "Dixie," or she would tear up a broom and put the straws one by one through the keyhole, where they fell in a little pile on the Royce's side. In time, Martha and the girls became more used to the sight and sound of this sorry madwoman. They lived from day to day being as cheerful as people who live on the slopes of an active volcano can be.

Almost daily they walked down to see their relatives and to talk matters over with them. The visits always lifted their spirits.

"If you can put up with that difficult situation until the end of the month, you will be with us then. I'll feel so much better when you're not under the same roof with that poor creature," Uncle John exclaimed.

"Her mother assures me that she is quite harmless," Martha replied.

"She snatched my bonnet off my head yesterday as I was going out to garden," complained Betsey, "and she does wail and moan so dreadfully. It was the longest time before I could go to sleep last night."

Betsey hoped it would be better when the month was over and they moved in with Uncle John and Aunt Claudia. She had forgotten that the shed room was so small. It was barely eight feet square and had two tiny windows — more like a jail cell than a room! At night it became an oven, and sleeping was really hard. Sally and Betsey wondered which was worse, the stifling hot shed room or the crazy lady they had just left.

Such food as the refugees were able to get was poor and meager. The great estates around them produced cotton, sugar cane, and corn. Fruit was of poor quality and vegetables, except for collards, were scarce. The same was true of milk and butter. What little poultry could be had was inferior quality, while eggs were an undreamed of luxury.

Since the winters were too warm to store ice, and the process of making ice was unknown, fresh meat was impossible to get. Supplies of regular groceries had been gone from Marshallville's one store for some time. On the table at mealtime was imitation coffee, cornbread, a small amount of wheat bread, excellent molasses, collard greens (a kind of coarse cabbage which the family came to hate), and salt pork (except in hot weather).

Hunger never left them. It was with them day and night—every bit as relentless as the Yankees.

The pretty color faded from Martha's cheeks and her heart ached as she watched her children growing thinner and knew the cause. Never in later years could Betsey stand to see food wasted, especially bread, which she came to view as somehow sacred.

The little girls soon made friends with the village children. Playing games helped them to forget their hunger. They had no toys except a broken-down locomotive which had been side-tracked not far from the house. It made a great plaything. The children climbed onto it and traveled far into unknown lands in their imagination. Felice, Betsey's cousin, had a fortune-telling doll, a small china doll placed at the center of a revolving disk on which verses were written. The disk was whirled, and when it stopped the doll pointed to a "fortune" on the disk. Betsey longed to possess this doll like nothing she had ever wanted before or in the years to come.

She finally confided in Sally, "If only I had that doll, I would be so happy. My blue ribbons would make her a beautiful dress. I know what I would name her—Georgia."

"But she belongs to Cousin Felice's fortuneteller," objected Sally.

"I know," replied Betsey, "but I'm going to ask Mother to buy it from her." However, cousin Felice proved quite unwilling to part with the little toy, and Betsey was forced to continue worshipping the doll from afar. Had Felice been able to look in Betsey's heart, she might have relented, but Betsey buried her disappointment so silently that her cousin never knew.

The children liked to watch the passing trains, some of which stopped at their station. The sight of rough coffin-boxes on the rear platforms of the cars became quite familiar to them, as did the sight of wounded soldiers who filled the cars. Ladies would bring fruit and flowers for the wounded. Betsey would give them tiny Confederate flags which she had made. The men would smile and put the flags in their hatbands.

"Uncle," Martha asked one day, "why do the freight cars go so heavily guarded? I have been noticing them for some time and wondering whether the enemy is near."

"No, he is not near," Uncle John replied, "at least not in the way that you mean. Those closed cars are filled with Yankee prisoners being taken to a prison about twenty-five miles from here—in Andersonville, I believe."

"I sure wish they were guarded more carefully," complained Aunt Claudia. "Two escaped when the train stopped yesterday and I'm afraid we'll be attacked."

"Now, Claudia, that's enough of such talk in front of the children."

"Yes," agreed Martha. "You two run outside and play."

Betsey's favorite playmate was Maud Gray, a child her own age, whose golden curls and sweet blue eyes delighted Betsey's aesthetic sense. On the first visit to Maud's home there were many things she wanted to show Betsey and Sally. There were strings of beautiful peppers, both red and yellow; gourds of all shapes, new kittens, flowers, a baby mule, and a mountain of peanuts in a shed.

"And now, maybe you'd like to see the dog," Maud suggested.

"Yes, I would," replied Betsey. "I like to play with dogs. I used to have a white poodle, but he ran away."

"This one can't run away," Maud told her. "He is chained all the time. He isn't the kind of dog you can play with, anyway. He has to have a keeper."

"I shouldn't think you'd like to have such a dog. What good is he?" Betsey asked.

"Well, you see," Maud replied, nodding her blond curls, "he isn't any use except when some of the Negroes run away to the swamps. Then he finds them and brings them out. Here he is," she added as they turned the corner of the barn.

A large vicious-looking black brute stirred as they came near. He came out from his kennel, rattling his heavy chain. Betsey was fascinated and started forward for a closer look.

"Be careful!" Maud cried, seizing her arm. "No one can touch him but his keeper." Just then the dog snarled and leaped at them to the length of his chain.

Two days later, Betsey went up to Maud's house alone. The house was the usual Southern type, standing on a high founda-tion with an open passage running straight through. As Betsey hopped up the stairs, she heard a deep growl and the rattling of a chain from the other end of the hallway. She looked up and saw that the black beast of a dog had torn loose from his kennel and was crouching to spring at her.

Betsey was paralyzed with fear. Unable to cry out or move, she stood face-to-face with certain death. The brute lunged toward her, howling savagely. But in that same instant, he was jerked back and fell to the floor. A piece of the kennel attached to the chain had caught around a pillar on the back porch and held him for an instant. That instant meant Betsey's salvation. Maud's older sister, her face white with horror, pulled the little girl into a room and slammed the door.

Uncle John heard of Betsey's escape that night as the family gathered around the fireplace.

"You may bless your lucky stars you were not torn to pieces, Betsey," he said. "That is the meanest dog in the whole county. Only a month ago he brought a man out of the swamps. I am told he was more than ready to come back after the dog got through with him."

A strange look that Aunt Claudia didn't like came over Uncle John's face as he was talking.

"Betsey, run off to bed," said Martha, noting her pale and shaken appearance. Martha watched her uncle as he strode up and down, his shaggy head bent forward. Then he began to speak again, this time half to himself.

"I tremble for my country when I reflect that God is just," he said, quoting Jefferson, "I tell you there is a day of wrath coming for all of us. We are living over a volcano and have been all our lives, just like the people who sang and danced under Vesuvius

WAYFARERS ONCE MORE

UNABLE TO CRY OUT OR MOVE, SHE STOOD FACE
TO FACE WITH CERTAIN DEATH. THE BRUTE
LUNGED TOWARD HER, HOWLING SAVAGELY.

until it poured forth and covered them over."

"I am sure I don't know what you mean, John," Claudia responded. "You talk very strangely."

"Just look at this little Marshallville," he continued, not paying attention to his wife. "Go up and down the streets and you will not find an able-bodied white man anywhere. All that's left are old men and boys, or men too feeble to fight. Then take a look at the plantations around. On the Baker place there are two hundred slaves; on the Miller place, three hundred, and so on. Among the black hundreds and thousands are many strong men. They have not sent their best into the army as we have, leaving only the young and infirm behind."

"Do be careful, John, and don't speak so loudly," Aunt Claudia warned uneasily as she got up and closed the doors. The others sat quietly, deep in the thoughts his words had aroused.

"You don't know anything about it, Martha," he went on, turning to his niece, "because in Tennessee you haven't so many of them and conditions are better. But here—he paused for a moment, then went on—there is no one who owns them by hundreds who hasn't always in his heart hid the secret dread of an uprising. It came in Haiti, and there is no reason it shouldn't come here. In fact, there is every reason why it should, except like the beasts of the field they don't know their own power."

"But, John," his wife protested, a scared look on her face, "I think most of them are much too attached to their masters to think of such a thing."

"Attached!" roared John Broyles with a great laugh. "How much attachment do you think that wretch feels who was dragged back by Gray's dog? And Carson doesn't even know his own slaves' names. He often meets them and asks to whom they belong. That's the plantation notion of a joke. The good-looking bright ones are picked out for house service, the others sent off to live in quarters near an overseer."

"But they were nothing but heathen savages in Africa before we brought them over and taught them to be Christians," insisted Aunt Claudia, tearfully.

Uncle John went over to a shelf and took down his violin. "Come, girls," he said gaily, "I have talked enough—perhaps too much. Let's amuse ourselves by dancing around the crater."

And so, putting aside their somber thoughts, the family arose and blithely danced to the merry strains of the fiddle.

Chapter Eight
❦ The Forgotten Corner ❦

ONE DAY IN EARLY SEPTEMBER, 1864, Betsey was watching a train stop and wondering if she should have brought her little flags to give to the wounded soldiers.

She forgot about the flags when she noticed a man in a worn gray uniform get off the train. It was unusual for anyone to get off the train in Marshallville, so Betsey couldn't help staring at him (even though she had been taught to *never* stare at people).

As he turned and started up the street, Betsey stared even harder, and then she knew—IT WAS HER FATHER! He saw her in the same instant and knelt down to enfold his daughter in a giant bear hug.

Betsey had so many things to tell her father, but she knew he was anxious to see Martha and Sally. She would wait until later. For now, it was just so good to walk beside him with his arm around her.

As soon as Martha saw them in the distance, she came running. Sobbing for joy, she was clasped in her husband's arms. Only Sally hung back a little, having forgotten her father's looks in the two years he had been away. She needed a little more time to make sure this man was really her father.

And Moses had to get used to seeing his "little girls" more grown up than when he left them. Ten-year-old Betsey and eight-year-old Sally could be thought of as "young ladies" rather than children. He was sad to realize how the war had robbed them of their childhood.

As his family led him into the house to receive the greetings of the others, they all wanted to hold his hands and were laughing and talking at once out of pure joy.

"Wherever did you come from, dear Moses?" was his wife's first question when they were all seated together. "And how did you find out where we were?"

"Following my escape, after much wandering and many adventures, I finally rejoined the army," Moses replied. "It is now in Macon, only about forty miles from here. For a long time, all my efforts to find you were unsuccessful. I learned that you had left East Tennessee and gone south, but 'the South,' as you know, is a pretty large place. At last, quite by accident, I got lucky. A man in my regiment, whose sister lives here, told me you were in Marshallville. I at once obtained leave of absence and here I am—ready to provide for the safety and welfare of my own."

That night, when the family gathered in the sitting room where the light of the pine knots flickered on the unpainted walls, Uncle John called on Moses to tell the story of his escape. So the returned warrior began his story:

"Much of my work was that of a scout. Having a good horse and knowing the country like a book, I was able to bring in a great deal of information. Generally, I had a few men with me, although sometimes I was alone. One day early in July I was out with three men, scouting in the vicinity of Franklin, when we found ourselves very near the enemy and were discovered.

"We turned and took flight, with the Yankees in close pursuit. I was almost to our lines when my horse accidentally fell into a ditch, which was hidden by high grass. I was thrown over his head. I could do nothing but put up my hands and stand still. They relieved me of the field glasses I had taken away from you, Martha. What I hated most was having to give up that fine revolver my brave little girls so gallantly captured, and which was passed on to me by the soldiers you met on your first night out of Franklin."

Betsey and Sally smiled and nudged each other.

"The rest of my party got safely away," Moses continued, "but I was taken to Nashville and put in the state penitentiary, which had been turned into a military prison. We were not badly off. There were four men in two good-sized rooms on the second floor. One room was directly over the driveway. From the driveway, a heavy door, which was locked and barred at night, opened directly onto the street.

"In the beginning, we were cheered up by friends who brought us treats, and by the expectation of parole or exchange. One of my prison mates was a young Spaniard who I asked to teach me Spanish. Another prisoner was an expert carver who made many pretty things out of odds and ends. Betsey, I brought you a brooch he carved from a mussel shell and I brought Sally a small paper knife carved from bone. You will hear about your gift later on, Martha.

"I was allowed to write my dear mother as long as the letter went unsealed. She sent me some comfortable Yankee clothing, shoes and many little things I needed. She overlooked that I was on the 'wrong side' of the war, and remembered only that I was her son.

"After several months had passed, we began to wonder why nothing happened. Were we to stay forever locked up? Then, all of a sudden, something did happen — to me. I was summoned to stand trial on a charge of guerilla warfare. I knew the accusation was serious, but I also knew it couldn't be proved. I was never anything but a scout.

"The trial was a farce from beginning to end. The witnesses made up their testimony, and one witness was someone I had supposedly killed! I was found guilty and sentenced to be executed, although no date was set. This was surprising, since guerillas were generally executed quickly. I began efforts on my own behalf. I wrote to my mother, and I wrote to you, Martha. Mother quickly urged my case on those of my family who had the most influence, and you, dear wife, went to Richmond. But we shall never know what the authorities decided because my roommates and I took matters into our own hands.

"We planned our escape carefully and, as it turned out, successfully. Ours is the only escape in my memory where all the preparations were done in broad daylight. We were lucky that our inner room was over the driveway.

"With a file a friend brought us concealed in a bouquet, we jagged a table knife into a crude saw and set to work cutting a hole through the floor of the inner room. The rattling of wagons going in and out over the cobblestones beneath drowned out the noise of our sawing.

"The job went slowly, but we had a lot of spare time. By February 25, a hole two feet square was cut. We held a council of war and decided we must wait for a stormy night to try our escape. On such a night, the sentry would go into his booth and few people would be on the street.

"The night of February 29 was a perfect stormy night. After the guard had made his last round and turned the key in the door of the outer room, we gathered nervously in the inner room. We knew this was our final act and we prayed it would be successful. The hole was ready except for the plaster, which had to be cut. The first piece of plaster had to fall to the ground, and that was when we all held our breath. If the guard saw it and then looked up to see where it had come from, it would be the end of our escape, and probably our lives.

"When that one piece of plaster fell, I thought I had never heard anything echo more loudly than it did as it dropped onto the cobblestones. The light from below shone up in our faces. A door opened and a guard came out. If he had looked up, the hole in the ceiling would catch his eye. But he looked around quickly and did not notice the plaster lying in the dust and dirt of the driveway. Seeing nothing, he went back to his room and closed the door.

"We worked rapidly, breaking up the plaster until the hole was fully opened. Then we tied blankets to form a rope and went down one by one. We slid open the bars across the door, and I turned the big key to unlock it. I put that great key into my pocket as a present for you, Martha.

"The storm swallowed us up so completely that by morning, when they discovered our escape, we were miles away, sheltered in the houses of our friends."

Betsey breathed a long sigh of satisfaction. The story had ended exactly right.

"I'm sure you found friends everywhere, Moses," Martha remarked.

"Yes, everywhere indeed," he replied. "They not only supplied all my needs, but they sheltered and hid me as well. In one place I had to lie down for a week until my feet healed. I had been so long in prison that they were very tender and soon blistered. Although they didn't dare keep me in the house, those kind people made quarters for me in the barn and fed me there."

When at last they were alone, Captain Royce and his wife had much to talk about—the past two years and plans for the future.

"I am convinced that this will not be a sheltered place much longer," said Moses. "Sherman is pressing steadily on. Already he is in possession of Atlanta. On the other hand, General Hood has fallen back to Macon and may move from there at any time. After all you have suffered, I am unwilling to see you again in the hands of the enemy."

"I am certainly willing to keep my distance from them," Martha responded. "That is why I am here. But I have been worried by news of the enemy's steady approach. You have arrived at just the right time, my dear Moses. I suppose we really should move to a safer place."

"Undoubtedly," he replied. "The only question is where?" And husband and wife fell silent, both thinking carefully.

"I think I have it," Moses said at last. "In the course of my wanderings, I came across a forgotten corner of southern Alabama, not far from the Mississippi line. I found a primitive plantation there. It wasn't grand, but I stayed there for several days. The owner, Mr. Oliver, was glad to have me. His wife had died and his daughter's husband was killed in battle. Both of them are sad and lonely and would appreciate your company."

"Can you write to Mr. Oliver and ask whether he will take us in as boarders?" Martha asked.

"No, mails are so uncertain these days I would rather go and talk to him directly. If he can't take us in, I will look around and find someone who can. It shouldn't take me too long. The railroads in that area have not been destroyed."

Moses left the next day and was back within a month. He brought good news to his anxious family.

"Mr. Oliver was most kind and obliging," he told his wife, "and so was his daughter, Mrs. Haley. Mrs. Haley has two little sons, and she expects another baby soon. They are looking forward to your arrival. Now, I must find the girls and tell them what a great surprise I have for them."

Betsey and Sally could hardly believe what their father told them. A pony all their own! Betsey finally stopped thinking about the fortunetelling doll.

"But where is the pony, Father?" they cried. "Can we see her now?"

"Not yet," he replied, "but pretty soon. I left her at Mr. Oliver's, where we are going tomorrow."

The Royces made the journey to Alabama in reasonable comfort. The country they traveled through had not been invaded, so they were able to take a train to Montgomery, then a boat to Selma, and rail again as far as Eutaw, where they took a stage coach for several miles. Finally, they hired a private carriage and rode across country into the "forgotten corner" of which Moses had told them. The scenery was flat and uninteresting, the roads heavy and sandy, the air close and lifeless, even in October. Martha was very glad when they finally stopped at Mr. Oliver's gate.

Before them stood a low, unpainted house with flowering shrubs planted thickly in front, above which rose slender chinaberry trees and a magnificent live oak just outside the gate. In back of the house were numerous shabby slave cabins and other buildings.

Sally whispered to Betsey, "I thought this was going to be a plantation like Walnut Hill, but it isn't *anything* like it."

"I know," Betsey whispered back in her sister's ear, "and that old man on the porch isn't at all like Grandfather."

"That old man" laid down his book and came to greet them. He was short, very heavy, and dressed in poorly fitting clothes. His dingy white shirt, open at the throat, was stained down the front with tobacco, as were his stubby fingers. His eyes showed a good-natured kindliness, which helped one overlook his less attractive features.

"This is Mr. Oliver," Moses whispered to his wife as he sprang from the carriage and went to meet their host.

"Delighted to see you, Captain," drawled the unkempt old man in his soft Southern voice. "I suppose you have brought your good lady and the little girls."

"I am very glad to meet you, ma'am," Mr. Oliver said, bowing in a courtly manner as he shook Martha's hand. "And I am also glad to welcome these little girls," he added, turning to shake their hands — to which Betsey and Sally made a polite reply, even though they wanted to giggle at the appearance of the funny-looking old man.

"My daughter is not at home, being away on a visit for a few days. But Melissa has your room ready. Come along in," the old man told them. Then, raising his voice, he called, "Here, you, Tim, Joe, Maggie and Sue; come take this lady's things into the house, and tell Diggs and Henry to carry in the trunks."

And so, followed by a troop of ragged slaves carrying carpet bags and the indispensable lunch basket, Mr. Oliver led the family inside.

The room reserved for the Royces was of very good size, with a ceiling of wood blackened with age and smoke. It was lit by two small windows facing onto little porches at the front and rear of the house. A large fireplace stretched across one end of the room. The furniture was simple and plain, consisting of a four-poster bed, a trundle bed, a washstand, and two chairs. The floor was bare, but white curtains hung at the windows.

"This is not bad," Martha said to Moses when they found themselves alone. "After the shed room, this seems very spacious. But isn't Mr. Oliver a picturesque specimen?"

Moses laughed. "His appearance might be improved upon," he said, "but he seems a kindly man, and his home offers you the shelter that you sorely need. His daughter is a very pretty woman."

Just then Melissa came to tell them that supper was ready, and they went into the dining room which opened off their room.

As the Royces entered, Mr. Oliver courteously motioned Mrs. Royce to the head of the table.

"Will you please sit there, ma'am, while my daughter's away?" he asked her. "It always looks better to see a lady at the head, eh, Captain?" So they all seated themselves, Mrs. Royce giving the girls a warning look as she saw questions forming.

Before beginning to pour the coffee, Martha looked to see what was in front of her. There was a large tin coffee pot filled with corn meal coffee, a china sugar bowl, no cream, six thin old silver spoons, two teacups, and three saucers — and five people to be served! Beckoning to one of the servants, Mrs. Royce said in a low voice, "I need three more cups and two saucers."

"Dere ain't no mo, missus," the girl replied.

The old man at the foot of the table looked up. "Our china has got down very low since the war began," he said, "and we don't seem to be able to get any more. If you give a cup to the Captain and keep one yourself, the little girls and I will have the saucers." With that he gave a friendly wink at the children.

Mrs. Royce, her face very red, began to do the old man's bidding. She thought to herself that the war must have found the family poorly supplied with china.

"Pass the cake, Matty," Mr. Oliver directed to one of the servants after the coffee had been passed around with as little spilling as possible. The girls looked up hopefully, strange as it seemed to start the meal with cake. A plate of round and somewhat greasy biscuits was brought in. After eyeing them dubiously, the girls looked to their mother for an explanation. Betsey kept quiet, but not Sally.

"Mother," she said in her high little voice, "I thought this was cake, but it's only biscuit."

Their host leaned back in his chair and laughed good-naturedly. "We call wheat bread 'cake' down here little girl," he explained, "and what you call 'cake' is 'sweet cake' with us. 'Bread' is always cornbread."

There was no butter on the table, its lack being supplied by a platter of fat bacon brimming with the grease fried out in the process of cooking. A jug of molasses completed the setting. Mr. Oliver spread his plate heavily with bacon grease and a portion of molasses, which he carefully stirred together. Then he sopped it up with his bread, to the wide-eyed astonishment of both children. Betsey, who was a small and dainty eater, just shuddered.

When the meal was over, the Royces returned to their room. Melissa had just finished lighting a fire, which blazed merrily on the hearth, sending its cheerful rays over the dark walls. It also was sending the temperature up by leaps and bounds, for the weather was unusually warm for October.

"Melissa!" Mrs. Royce said sharply as she felt the heated air. "Why are you lighting a fire? We are not cold."

"No, missus," Melissa replied, "I know that. I jus lights it to give light."

"But a candle will do just as well, and better in this warm weather. Bring me a candle."

"I can't do that, missus," Melissa answered, shaking her head, "My missus ain't got no candles, 'cept for the table, and we always burns a few pi-knots fo light in the rooms." So saying, she picked up her basket of "pi-knots" and left.

Moses looked depressed. The living conditions were not what he had hoped them to be.

"I don't like leaving you here," he said dejectedly, while seating himself as far from the fire as possible. "I'm afraid you are not going to be comfortable. I think I'll go over to Mr. Coleman's tomorrow and see if he'll take you. He is only four miles away, and his place has a better appearance."

"Don't worry, Moses," his wife responded trying to cheer him up, "Remember, the mistress of the house is away, and when she returns I'm sure things will improve. But Moses was not reassured, and was determined to look for a better place in the morning.

Early in the morning, the family was awakened by a muffled thumping and banging coming from somewhere quite near their room.

"What is that confounded noise?" Moses asked crossly. "It has been going on steadily for almost an hour."

"It sounds like a loom, or rather, several of them," Martha replied. She was familiar with the sound. "They must be very close by."

Moses did not succeed in finding another place for his family. After a few days, he had to leave them with a heavy heart. He consoled himself with the thought that at least they were safe, and with Mrs. Haley's return things might improve.

At the end of that week, Mrs. Haley did return with her two little boys and a nurse not any better in appearance than the untidy Melissa. Mrs. Haley was as pretty as Moses had said. She had good features, soft brown hair, and pleasing hazel eyes. However, her smooth, pale complexion and the whites of her eyes had taken on a yellow tinge as the result of snuff-dipping, a habit to which she was addicted.

THE FORGOTTEN CORNER

Martha Royce prided herself in being a good judge of character, and she soon formed her estimate of their hostess: "Shallow, hard and shrewish," she said to herself early on, and never had cause to change her opinion.

Food rations were cut down for the slaves and the Royces. While the food portions decreased, the loom activity escalated, with strict demands for ever-increasing production.

"That woman has the soul of a miser," Martha observed as she came to know more about Mrs. Haley. One night, Mrs. Haley's voice was heard in loud and angry argument with her father. The looms had stopped their banging for the day, the work was inspected, and the black weavers had gone to their quarters.

"I tell you, Pa," Mrs. Haley was saying in her high voice, "Jane is a full yard short of her task."

Mr. Oliver's voice responded, evidently excusing the woman, although his words could not be understood.

"I don't believe she's sick at all," cried Mrs. Haley. "They're always faking, and if I paid any attention to that I'd never get any work done. She's got to be punished, so you just go to their quarters and whip her."

Again there came the murmur of Mr. Oliver's voice.

"If you won't go, I will!" declared his daughter, rising. Since she was very close to the birth of her baby, the old man reluctantly got up, took his whip from the wall, and shuffled out of the house.

"Mother," Betsey whispered, horror written on her face, "this makes me feel sick all over. I just can't bear it!" She began to sob. "Imagine Grandfather doing such a thing!"

"He never did," replied her mother. "His slaves were never so much as struck, although sometimes the little ones were corrected, just as I correct you. I don't think Mr. Oliver will whip her very hard, since he didn't want to go in the first place," Martha said to console Betsey.

Christmas Day, 1864, dawned forlornly. Instinctively, the children felt the uselessness of hanging up stockings. They knew there would be no gifts, so they were not disappointed. It proved to be an almost barren day. Mrs. Haley's little boys, who had been given two sticks of candy each, came in and gave half a stick to Betsey and Sally, prompted by their grandfather. This act of generosity shot a solitary ray of light across that cheerless Christmas.

One morning early in January, Betsey woke up to see her mother, fully dressed, coming into their room from the dining room. Betsey sat up, at once wide awake. The past three years had taught her to dread the unexpected.

"What has happened, Mother?" she asked.

"Nothing has happened," Mrs. Royce answered. "At least nothing alarming. Mrs. Haley had a little baby boy."

I'm so glad!" Betsey exclaimed. "I'd like to go in and see him."

"After a while you may," her mother replied.

Martha Royce's heart stirred with pity for the young widow, whose tears fell when she saw the resemblance of the baby to her dead husband, and realized that the child would never know his father.

THE FORGOTTEN CORNER

SOMETIMES THEY MADE DARING EXPLORATION
TRIPS ACROSS THE FIELDS. THEY WERE
ALWAYS ON THE LOOKOUT FOR PATCHES OF RICE
FOR DOLLY TO GRAZE ON.

While Martha tended to Mrs. Haley, Betsey and Sally were spending time with the pony they had named "Dolly." They rode along all the roads and lanes nearby, always bareback since they had no saddle. Sometimes they made daring exploration trips across the fields. They were always on the lookout for patches of rice for the pony to graze on.

When they weren't riding Dolly, they were busy making their own toys—little wagons from boxes, with corn cobs for wheels, and dolls from forked sticks.

Martha strictly forbade Betsey and Sally to play with the Negro children after the day Evelina stole Sally's choicest corncob cart and then lied about it. "I am sorry for the poor creatures," Martha said to herself, "but my first duty is to protect my little girls."

One day, the girls came soberly to their mother as she sat working in her room. "What is the matter, children?" she asked.

"Mother," Betsey told her, "Melissa's boy Fred, the one who has fits, fell over on a pot of hot water in the kitchen this morning and was badly scalded."

"Where is he?" asked Mrs. Royce. "Perhaps I can give some advice about him."

"They have him in a corner of the loom house where Melissa can look after him when she's weaving," Betsey replied. Then, hesitating a moment, she looked at Sally. "What Sally and I wanted to know," she went on, "was if you would let us save one of our biscuits for him at each meal. I am sure he won't have any good things given him, and he is dreadfully hurt."

Martha was taken aback and did not answer at once. The little girls were insufficiently fed and showed it, and one biscuit meant half their portion. Still—a better thought came into her mind—"life is more than meat."

"Yes," she said with a little pang in her heart, "you may if you wish. You can take turns." And this they did until Fred was well again.

The winter proved very mild in that far southern spot. Snowflakes were seen only once. By the middle of April, the sun shone with the warmth of summer. One day, as Betsey sat by the window working on her arithmetic, Sally, who had gone outside to play, came bursting in round-eyed and scared. Her face was hotly flushed.

"What is the matter, child?" Martha asked anxiously. "You look frightened."

Gasping, Sally approached her mother and stammered, "Mother, th—the Negro children are running around without a speck of clothes on!"

"Sally!" cried Mrs. Royce, amazed, "it can't be! You must be mistaken."

Betsey looked out the window. "No, she isn't, Mother," she said. "There goes Evelina now, all naked. She is just hiding behind a bush."

Mrs. Royce laid down her work and went out. Sally was not mistaken! All the boys and girls ten years old and under were, indeed, running about in a state of complete nudity. At first, they were shy and hid behind bushes and outbuildings. Then, gradually, this wore off until at last they conducted themselves with an easy unconsciousness as must have belonged to our first parents. It was a great savings of clothes, Mrs. Haley explained, since the children didn't put them on till the first frost.

Sally and Betsey would always remember the first warm day of 1865 at the Oliver plantation in that forgotten corner of southern Alabama.

Chapter Nine
❧ The Day of Reckoning ❧

THE BLOODY DRAMA OF FOUR YEARS was drawing to a close. Sherman had given President Abraham Lincoln a Christmas present of the city of Savannah. The crippled Confederacy lay in its death struggle. Around Richmond, the last act was being played out, the final curtain about to descend.

In the "forgotten corner" there was little news. What news they had was badly distorted. Martha knew for a fact that a major battle had been fought in Franklin, and that Moses was not there. She knew he was unable to join General John Bell Hood from two letters he had written her. Several months had passed since she received those letters.

The residents at the Oliver plantation received no real news, since the local gazettes were the only available source. These were of little value, as were the rumors regarding both armies.

One day in early April, a body of Confederate troops in search of food, fresh horses, mules, and other supplies suddenly appeared at Mr. Oliver's house. They belonged to General Nathan Bedford Forrest's cavalry command, who were camped a few miles away. Their clothes were sadly worn and ragged, their shoes old and broken. In some cases they rode with feet bare and bleeding in the stirrups. During this time, many soldiers visited at the house.

Among them was a stalwart young Texas Ranger, Private Bates, with whom Betsey and Sally struck up an immediate friendship, based on their mutual love of horses. Private Bates had a large gray horse, Raccoon, of whom he told wonderful stories. The girls had fun sharing their stories about Dolly. When the Texan learned that the Royces had come from Tennessee, he at once exclaimed, "Franklin! I certainly ought to know that name, because the surgeon of our regiment comes from there."

Martha pricked up her ears. "What is his name?" she asked.

"Bailey, ma'am, Dr. Bailey. And a mighty fine doctor he is. He brought me through when I was wounded. Perhaps you know him, ma'am?"

"I surely do," replied Mrs. Royce. "He was a young man just beginning practice. We preferred an older man with experience."

"He's had plenty of experience by now, ma'am," the Texan observed with a laugh. "You just ought to see a field hospital after a battle, with the doctors busy chopping and sawing. They wanted to take off my leg—limb, I mean—but I swore I'd kill the first man who did it. They were in such a hurry, you know, ma'am," he added by way of apology, "that they couldn't be very particular. But a leg's—I mean, a limb's a limb and I only had two."

"When you see Dr. Bailey, won't you tell him we are here and ask him to ride over and see us?" asked Mrs. Royce. And the Texan promised he would.

The next day, the young doctor gaily cantered up to the house. Throwing his bridle reins over a fence post, he ran up the walk.

Since Betsey knew him, she came out to meet him. Shyly, she held out her hand of welcome.

"Howdy, howdy, sissy," he cried, lifting her up and kissing her soundly. "You remind me of dear old Franklin, the land of my birth. See what I brought you." He fished in his coat pocket while Betsey eagerly waited. Then he brought forth a large white goose egg. It wasn't exactly what Betsey was expecting, but she thanked him politely as she took the big egg.

"Where did you get that egg, George?" called Mrs. Royce as she came from the house, smiling, "I am sure you stole it."

"Nothing of the kind, Mrs. Royce," he said as they shook hands. "You do me a grave injustice. It just came my way. If you will roast it, Betsey, you will find it to be very good," he insisted as they went into the house.

"Tell me the news from Franklin," said Mrs. Royce. "I have been an exile so long that I am eager for any news of the dear place. I hear a great battle has been fought there."

"Yes," the doctor responded soberly, "it was a very great fight—one of the bloodiest of the war. Many of Hood's men were Franklin boys or from the country around there, and they fought like madmen in sight of their homes. I am told that one of the deadly incidents of that day was at your Osage Orange hedge."

"How could that be?" asked Mrs. Royce in surprise. "I know I had a good deal of hedging all around the place, besides two cross-division hedges, but I hardly see how that could make for a deadly incident."

"Before the Confederate attack began," Dr. Bailey explained, "the Union troops cut down the entire hedge and laid it in a long row across Carter's field, just in front of the entrenchments they had thrown up before the battle. The tall green grass hid the Osage, which of course was green also. When the Confederates charged the entrenchments, they were tangled in the thick, thorny hedge and held there under the enemy's point-blank fire, like flies stuck to flypaper! I have heard that the hedge caused the loss of more lives than any other event of the day, and that is why I called it a deadly incident." (See pg. 197).

"How I wish we had cut that hedge down before the war," exclaimed Martha. "I can't bear to think of our brave men dying because of that hedge."

"My folks were there," George said, "but escaped harm, since our house was not in the line of heaviest fire. The Carters, however, were directly on the firing line. Fortunately, their house is built of brick. The walls are pocked by bullets from top to bottom. The gatepost was so full of lead that a Union officer shipped it north as a keepsake."

"I suppose, of course, that our house disappeared long ago," sighed Mrs. Royce. "Sena Clouston wrote soon after we left to tell me that the soldiers were pulling it to pieces for use in the camp."

"It was bound to go sooner or later," Dr. Bailey admitted. "If it had escaped the soldiers, it would have been destroyed in the battle. A line of breastworks (see Appendix) runs across your lot, and the whole place is as bare as my hand; not a bush or tree remains, I hear, nor a fence, nor indeed anything to tell that on that site once stood one of the prettiest homes in Franklin."

Martha Royce sighed, not trusting herself to dwell on what the future might hold for her family. Even if the cause she loved won, her sacrifices could never be repaid. And if the South lost...? "What is to be the end, George?" she asked. "Can we win? What is the latest news? We hear so little here."

"Your questions are not easy to answer," the young doctor replied gravely. "Every kind of news is afloat, most of it false on its face. But Savannah and Charleston fell long ago — that much is certain — and we hear Lee is hard pressed in Virginia. One of the most sinister signs is the conduct of our own soldiers, who are discouraged and rapidly becoming lawless. Many are deserting, but we can scarcely blame them. I don't think Forrest has lost many, but that is the story from other parts.

"Why the Negroes don't make trouble I can't understand; but so far they have behaved very well. Surely the war cannot last much longer. The South, at least, is almost exhausted. I believe we shall hear peace declared before the end of the summer."

The Royces were sorry when Forrest's command moved out and they said goodbye to Dr. Bailey. On the heels of their departure came wild and sudden rumors of a raid by Union troops, almost in sight of "the forgotten corner."

Martha Royce faced the news calmly. All that she experienced in Franklin at the start of the war prepared her for whatever was ahead. But Mrs. Haley and her father were in a state of panic. Each reacted in a unique manner, according to his or her personality.

Mrs. Haley wrung her hands and told Martha how scared she was because she'd "never seen a Yankee up close." Mrs. Royce assured her the Yankees would not kill her, but she had better hide her valuables. Her advice was taken and the "treasures" were buried by Mrs. Haley.

A different reaction from Mr. Oliver resulted in his leaving to hide in the swamp. He had consumed more than enough peach brandy for the trip. Waving three guns, he made a courtly bow in Mrs. Royce's direction and left.

The panic proved to be quite without cause. The Union troops did not come at all. Mr. Oliver soon returned from his swamp hiding place, sober and minus one gun. He never was able to account for the missing firearm. That same week, he and his daughter went away for a day to visit a relative.

"You aren't afraid to be left alone for a little, are you Mrs. Royce?" Mr. Oliver asked her. "My daughter and I will be back by sundown." Mrs. Royce assured him that she felt no fear, so the two departed.

The day passed uneventfully. When the sun was setting and it grew too dark to sew, Mrs. Royce went into the parlor and opened the piano. With the children sitting beside her, she began to play and sing "Rock Me to Sleep, Mother," Betsey's favorite, which always made her a little teary. Then it was "Lorena," sweet and mournful, and "Lulu is Gone," over which Betsey puzzled considerably, trying to understand why and where "Lulu" had gone.

While still thinking about Lulu, Betsey happened to look up and was startled to see dark forms crowding onto the little front porch. Then they moved into the passageway between the parlor and the Royce's room. They finally began to enter the sacred area of the parlor itself. It was the slaves, just in from work in the fields—men who were never allowed away from their quarters and who were probably inside their master's house for the first time in their lives.

Instantly, that sinister shadow of the South—the Great

Dread—gripped Betsey's heart. Leaning closer to her mother, she whispered a warning in her ear.

Mrs. Royce's composure did not forsake her, even though the words of her Uncle John flashed across her mind: "We are living over a volcano!" She finished the last verse of "Lulu," then closed the piano and said to the children, "That is enough for tonight." Then, taking them by the hand, she passed through the black men as though she did not see them, went into her room, and closed and locked the door.

The audience disappeared as quietly as it had come. When the master and mistress returned, all was as usual.

As April drew to a close, rumors of disaster came thick and fast, with the persistent report of General Robert E. Lee's surrender. Bands of aimless, lawless men passed and re-passed day and night. Mr. Oliver sent his horse, mules, and the pony, Dolly, to a hiding place in the canebrake.

One day early in May, Betsey came running into her mother's room. She was waving a blue envelope. "Mother! Mother!" she cried joyfully. "I have a letter! Mr. Oliver just gave it to me. Please won't you read it to me? The writing is so funny I'm afraid I can't make it out."

"I wonder who could be writing to you, Betsey," Martha replied. She turned the letter over and studied the signature at the end. "Why, it's your friend Bates, the Texas Ranger. It is signed "John R. Bates," and he is the only Bates we know. Let's hear what he has to say."

A GENTEEL SPY

Unfolding the letter, this is what she read:

Bluffporte, Ala.
May 1, 1865

Miss Betsey Royce,

Maddam it is with the greatest of plesur I take my pen in hand to write a few lines to let you know I have not forgot you and Sally I passed in eight miles of you the other day. I thought I would call to see you all but I found et would be empossible for me to do so. I hope I will be able to meet you sum day, when you can play me sum pretty paces on the piano.

Miss Betsey I think you and Sally are the pretis little girls I ever met with in all my roundes. I hope you will not forget me as long as life last to you. I cant help feeling for you.

I have but little knuse to write there are veres rumors afoot, grate meney people think the Gen Lee has surrendered his holw army but et is all Yankee lies ever word of it, Gen Lee is to grate a general to surrender as noble an army as the army of northern Virginia.

We have et from southern scores that lee and Grant has ben fighting. Grant has lost n battle and by desertion some hundred thousand men and et is thought by grate meney that we will have pease soon. I think we will have an armistes for 40 days is all the nuse I have.

Miss Betsey I have swaped off Raccoon. I don't think I will ever get a horse that I could think half as much of as I thought of him. I could not help sheding tears when

THE DAY OF RECKONING

I parted with him. I got as fine mule as I ever saw, the mule rides fine is very large but I think ef I had my horse back he would die mine, but the best of friends must part in time of war. I realy hope that you will keep your little Dollie as long as life lasts.

Miss Betsey I haven't heard of my command yet. I hope you will remember me in your tender and sweet prares. I think I would be sweetly blessed if sum pretty little girls would remember me as a grate and good soldier, feel that I was true to my colors, and that they had been protected by my strong arms and willing heart. I can say with a clear heart that I have discharge all my duties as a soldier, grate meney say they entend to quit fighting, but I can assure you that my heart has never bin as much as shuck, yet as to submission as long as I can meet good ladies as your mother I entend to stand as a stone wall struggling for liberty.

Well I must close my trifling letter. I hope you will excuse my bad writing and spelling, give my love to your mother, sister and widow. I truly hope that you will soon return to your sweet home and dwell in pease at home. Ef I knew where to tell you to write I would ask you to write me. May god bless you is my prares.

Farewell. I am yours truly

John R. Bates

His heart is in the right place, even if his writing and spelling are peculiar, Martha thought as she handed the letter back to Betsey.

"It was kind of Mr. Bates to remember a little girl like you," she said aloud, "and if I were you I would put the letter away carefully and keep it."

Betsey followed her mother's advice, and years later her children found much amusement in its odd spelling and cramped writing. She herself wondered what had become of the brave warm-hearted Texan, who, like the clerk in *The Merchant of Venice*, "took some pains in writing."

A few days after the letter came, Martha was sitting on the front porch when Mr. Oliver rode up. He dismounted and walked slowly toward the house. His bowed head and dragging footsteps told her he was the bearer of bad news. His eyes met Martha's as he came closer, and his daughter came out on the porch.

"It's all over," he said heavily. "No mistake about it this time. Lee surrendered two weeks ago. THE CAUSE IS LOST!" Heaving a giant sigh, he dropped into a chair and buried his face in his hands.

His daughter looked at him, dazed for a moment. Then she broke into speech.

"Lost? Lost?" she cried, "Then I suppose we won't have a single slave left!"

Martha quietly folded her work, got up without a word, and went into her room. Her little girls, playing with their imitation dolls, looked up when they saw her. Betsey saw how pale her mother looked. She put down her doll and went to her side.

"What is it, Mother?" she asked quietly.

"Lee has surrendered," her mother answered in a voice unfamiliar to Betsey. Then, to Betsey's horror, her mother dropped into a chair by the bed, threw her arms on the bed, and burst into tears. Betsey looked on helplessly at her mother's shaking body, while listening to sobs she had never heard before.

During the past four years, Martha Royce had suffered endless hardship and loss. She had seen the shadow of death draw near and then back off, but her perceptive blue eyes had shed no tears. Now that "The Cause" for which she had sacrificed so dearly was lost, the tears flowed freely.

Timidly, Betsey drew near and touched her mother. "Mother, Mother," she cried in a quavering voice. Receiving no reply, she began to cry as well. Little Sally, dismayed at their crying, burst into tears without quite knowing why.

For the next few weeks, a kind of vague uncertainty hung over the plantation. Even the slaves in their ignorance sensed that something unusual had taken place. Although the looms still banged, it was with diminished energy, and the men in the fields felt the master's rule to be less stern than of old.

The slaves talked together, waiting for they knew not what. They had no concept of a life as a free individual. Regardless, they felt a change coming and sensed that their lives would never again be the same.

Mr. Oliver and his daughter had many talks regarding the slaves. As their voices became more argumentative, Mrs. Royce could not help but hear how each one felt. Mrs. Haley, to no surprise, was all for letting matters go on with the slaves just as if they had not been freed.

"They have no idea they are free," she argued, "so why say anything to them? They are better off here than anywhere else. They are no more fit to take care of themselves than my little boys.

Slaves have no sense anyway."

Mr. Oliver was not unwilling to follow his daughter's advice, but he saw difficulties.

"We can't keep the news from them," he said. "Two of Coleman's slaves were over here yesterday talking to ours. They are all beginning to realize they are free. I can see it already in their actions. I am going to call them together after dinner, give them a talk and then hire them all to stay on. After all, I needn't pay them much," he ended somewhat apologetically.

Even so, Mrs. Haley was not happy about hiring those she had formerly owned. Tearfully, she protested that they would be utterly ruined.

Mr. Oliver ignored his daughter and called the slaves together. He stood on the front porch to address them. At his request, Mrs. Royce and her children were present, as well as Mrs. Haley.

The looms were still, the mules stood unharnessed in the stable, and the plows lay idle while the slaves stood before "the master."

The war was over, he told them, the South had lost and they were free. Even though they were free, they must continue to work. No one could live without doing so. Since the crops in the fields were growing and must be tended, he wanted to hire them all to stay on with him. He named a small monthly fee for the grown men and women, offering to keep the children for what little they could do. Then, to Mrs. Royce's great surprise, he ended by saying, "I will hire all of you but Melissa. Her I don't want."

The reason for this, Mrs. Royce never discovered, though she may have had her ideas. Mr. Oliver, influenced partially by his daughter, had been a hard master. His slaves were treated little better than beasts of the field. It had been in his interest to keep them as ignorant as possible, and he considered them to be wholly amoral. Since they could think of no other place to be, one by one they accepted their master's terms and chose to stay on. Melissa alone wandered forth into the unknown world.

One long, hot July day was drawing to a close. Betsey sat by the window with her arithmetic on her lap. She had just finished studying a problem where a man leaves an estate to be divided up between his wife, five sons, and three daughters. She glanced ahead to the next problem, which compared the speed of a greyhound to that of a deer. Since she wasn't interested in calculating the comparative speeds of the deer and greyhound, her mind took a different turn.

She looked at her mother and asked, "Mother, are we rich?"

Mrs. Royce looked up in surprise and hesitated, not knowing how much it was wise to tell the child. "Betsey," she said at length, "you are old enough to know something of our circumstances. Even if I didn't want to tell you, it would be impossible for you not to know. We are very far from rich. All we possess in this world is four acres of land in Franklin."

"But Mother," Betsey objected, "How can you be poor when you have so much money in your trunk?"

Martha answered Betsey by going to her trunk and unlocking it. She took out a great roll of Confederate money and handed it to Betsey. "You and Sally may have this paper. Since the South has failed, we haven't a single real dollar. I ought to have paid Mr. Oliver for our board the first of July, but I could not. He was very kind and said he would wait till your father comes."

"When is Father coming?" Betsey asked.

"I cannot tell," her mother replied. "I heard from him last when he was in Tennessee, but that was three months ago. There's been nothing since."

Betsey sighed and once more looked out the window with a troubled expression on her face.

"Now that the sun is setting, it is cooler," said her mother. "Call Sally and we'll go out for a walk."

The three went out of the gate beneath the great live oak and down the dusty lane past the cotton gin. Sally and Betsey were walking ahead of Martha when they suddenly cried out, "Look, Mother, look! There's Father!"

Their mother looked where they were pointing, to a ragged, dirty-looking man. "Hush, girls," she said sternly, "That's not your father. That's just another worn out soldier on his way home."

Betsey and Sally were silent for a moment, but unconvinced. All of a sudden they broke away from their mother and went racing up the road to meet the stranger. He lifted up each little girl to hug and kiss her.

Martha needed no further convincing. She saw her girls were right all along. Her dear husband was home at last. A dirty, ragged, and sun-burned Moses Royce held his wife and children with strength that belied his walking sixty miles that day!

"I would have come sooner," Moses said to his wife as they walked toward the house with her clinging to his arm, "But it takes a long time to travel as I have done. Having no

THE DAY OF RECKONING

IT WAS FATHER! ...HE LIFTED UP EACH
LITTLE GIRL TO HUG AND KISS HER.

money, I had to make the journey on foot. I have walked five hundred miles."

Martha looked at him without speaking, the tears rising slowly in her eyes.

"I have passed through a stricken country, bare and desolate," he went on, "by battlefields planted thick with graves; over stretches ten miles at a time where I saw no inhabited house, only those standing empty with broken wide-open doors. Or else there were blackened chimneys where dwellings once had been. The South lies in ruins." He paused, and they walked slowly on for a few moments in silence, the children quietly following.

Then Martha Royce lifted her head and spoke, with hope and courage shining in her face: "The South is in ruins, as you say," she answered, "and the Cause on which we staked all is lost; but the future belongs to us, whatever it may hold. We are young and strong; we have our children; and we are together again, saved from many perils.

"Please God, we will never be parted again."

Chapter Ten
❧ Reunited ❧

ON THE EVENING OF MOSES' RETURN, the family went to their room as soon as possible after supper. The minute the door closed, Moses gave vent to his growing indignation. "How you have endured this place for all these months I cannot see!" he exclaimed.

"There was nothing else to do," Martha replied quietly. "It was that or live in the open."

"But why do they live this way with a plantation at their service and plenty of labor?" Moses persisted.

"Partly a low standard of living, I suppose," Martha answered, "and partly bad management. Also, Mrs. Haley is very frugal, as you have doubtless observed."

"Don't worry about it, Father," Betsey interjected happily. To her the discomfort of the past year seemed slight now that her father had returned. "We are used to being hungry, and we don't mind it so much."

"I do!" cried Sally, stomping her foot. "I just hate being hungry."

Moses smiled at his daughter. "Never mind, Sally dear, we needn't think about what we don't like here. Much more important is what we're going to do next."

The Royces were quiet, each lost in his or her own thoughts.

Betsey wasn't ready to think about the future. She was basking in the comfort of her father's presence and his return from the war. She couldn't help noticing how different her father looked from the morning he rode away to war. Then he was wearing his new gray uniform Martha had made for him. Betsey remembered how proud she was that she was allowed to sew the red braid on his shirts when she was only seven. Now his clothes were all ragged, and his shoes.... Betsey's aesthetic sense was still with the new gray homespun and handsome red braid as she took another look at her father's feet. Remnants of leather barely covered them. His toes had worn through, and the bottoms of his feet were beginning to show.

"Father!" she cried in horror, "Just look at your shoes. What has happened to them? There's almost nothing left!"

Moses smiled and looked down thoughtfully at his feet. "I wonder how many miles I have walked in these? They are the same ones my dear mother sent me when I was in prison two years ago. And ever since my escape I have been walking, walking, walking. "But you know, Betsey," he continued with a twinkle in his eye, "they are in pretty good shape when you think how many people are without any shoes."

Martha, who had been deep in thought during Betsey's talk with her father, brought their attention back to the major problem: "How will we get back to Franklin? At the moment, we have nothing in all the world but four acres of land in Franklin, Tennessee."

"Not quite all, Martha dear," her husband said quietly, "at least not since yesterday. When I reached the Hollow Square post office there was a letter waiting for me from Edmond, my brother-in-law (See Appendix). It contained a draft for two hundred dollars. We have enough real money to get back to Franklin, provided we're careful."

"What a wonderfully kind thing for your relatives to do, Moses!" Martha exclaimed. "Do you still have the letter? I should like to hear it."

Moses read aloud for all to hear:

New Orleans, La.
July 6, 1865

Dear Moses,

The fight is over and it only remains for us to shake hands and start over again, which I am sure we will both do. Included is a draft for $200, which any bank will cash for you. It is a joint gift from your mother, Jane, and me. We know that the bottom has fallen out of the South and we suppose that you and your family are stranded at Hollow Square, where we last heard from you. I suppose you will return to Franklin. My work here is drawing to an end and I expect to be mustered out soon. After that, I shall take my family back to Rutland.

Let us hear from you.

Yours,

Edmond Morse

"Bless him," Martha said quietly. "Little does he know how completely the bottom has fallen out for us. But it is more than kind of your relatives to have cared about us — it is a godsend!"

"Yes. You know, as I read the letter, the words of the Psalmist came to me: 'Bless the Lord, O my soul, and forget not his benefits,'" said Moses. "We have been wonderfully provided for. But it remains for us to plan a cheap journey home."

The next morning, the Royces continued their conference in the stifling heat of their room. The air was stagnant, since there were only two small windows for ventilation. Being so uncomfortable energized them to form their travel plans as quickly as possible.

"Is it too far to walk?" inquired little Sally, who was anxious to be off at once.

"Rather," replied her father, winking at Betsey. "Franklin is about three hundred miles from here."

"I suppose the railroads are out of the question," Martha remarked, taking up the darning (see Appendix) she had laid aside the night before.

"Practically, they are." Her husband answered.

"Well, if that is the case, and it's too far to walk," Martha went on with a smile at Sally, "then the only thing is to drive."

"That is the conclusion I had reached," said Moses, "and I imagined you would agree with me."

The children clapped their hands. "Fine!" they cried together. "We'll drive the pony."

"The pony is alright as far as she goes," replied their father, "but she could hardly survive three hundred miles pulling all of us. Somewhere, somehow, I must find a team."

"If you can find a wagon and two horses, I think we'll be able to manage," Martha suggested. "We'll buy food along the way and camp out at night. That way there will be no hotel bills. But you'll have to inquire around for a wagon. I'm sure Mr. Oliver has none and, if he had, he would want double the price."

"Demopolis is the nearest town of any size," Moses went on, "about thirty miles from here, I believe. Tomorrow I shall walk over there and get Ed's draft cashed, and then inquire about a wagon and horses. A good deal of Confederate army equipment has been turned in there, so I'm told."

He hesitated a moment and then added, "I must go there anyway to be sworn in." (see Appendix)

"What do you mean, 'sworn in?'" Martha asked suspiciously. The children gazed inquiringly at their father.

"I would never do it—never, never!" Martha declared, her eyes defiant. The little girls stirred uneasily. Moses sat silent awhile, then spoke with decision.

"I can understand just how you feel, Martha," he said, "but we may as well face the situation as it is. The South played for heavy stakes and lost. It remains for her to accept defeat, bitter though it be—she has no alternative. *Vae victis.*"

"I wonder what that means," Betsey whispered to Sally.

"I don't know," Sally whispered back, "and I don't care."

Moses stood up and began to prepare his consoling smoking pipe. "I shall start for Demopolis tomorrow as early as I can," he told his family, "and return as quickly as possible. Then we'll be off on our journey home."

The little girls smiled happily, and their mother raised her bowed head. "We have ourselves at any rate, and nothing that can be confiscated. So I guess we're ready to begin life over again as soon as we find out how and where."

"One day at a time, my dear," her husband replied. "Tomorrow, I shall make the first move."

The following afternoon, Moses went to Demopolis, a small town under normal circumstances. With Confederate soldiers taking their oath of allegiance to the Union, the town had swelled in number and activity. Moses found the office of the Adjutant and was directed to the Captain, who sat at a desk littered with papers and books. Looking up at Moses, the Captain asked curtly,

"What do you want?"

"I have come to take the oath of allegiance," Moses replied. The Captain turned to his assistant, who at once produced a blank form and handed it to Moses.

"Read it over," he commanded. "Are you quite prepared to take this oath?"

"Yes, sir, I am," Moses replied.

"Under whom did you serve during the war?" the officer asked.

"Under General Hood."

"Sign here," the Captain barked, thrusting a pen into Moses' hand and indicating a blank space. Moses obeyed.

The assistant then read aloud the oath while Moses stood with raised hand and affirmed it. Finally, the Captain affixed his signature and handed the paper to Moses. "Carry that in your pocket," he ordered, and turned back to his work.

REUNITED

The paper read as follows:

I, Moses Royce, do solemnly swear in the presence of Almighty God that I will hereafter defend the Constitution of the United States and the Union of the States hereunder; and that I will in like manner abide by and support all laws and proclamations which have been made during the existing rebellion with reference to the emancipation of slavery. So help me God.

Moses Royce

Sworn and subscribed to before me at Demopolis, Alabama, this 27th day of July, A.D. 1865.

J.G. McGraw
Captain, & A.A.A. Gen.

Earlier that day, as he entered Demopolis, Moses had noticed a large lot filled with wagons of all sorts, all in bad shape and some hopelessly disabled. Upon leaving the Captains' office, he learned that the lot had been used by the Confederates but was now abandoned. He made his way out there, found the soldier in charge, and made his wants known.

"I shall be glad to pay you for a wagon," he said. "I need one to carry my wife and children back to Tennessee."

"There's nothing for sale here," the soldier replied, "but if you can patch up a wagon out of all this rubbish, you are welcome to it."

Moses was no wagon builder, but at the end of two days, with the advice — and sometimes the assistance — of spectators, he had assembled something unlike any wagon built before or since. Even so, it looked as if it would serve the purpose. The iron parts had been so heated by the July sun that they could not be handled until cooled by water; the wheels were strong, but did not match; and there was no wagon bed. Still, on the whole, Moses was pleased with the result.

For a small sum, he bought a tall black army horse named Frank. Moses then patched together enough harness for two horses. He tied a tongue for a prospective team to the wagon, got Frank adjusted to himself and a pair of shafts, and drove contentedly out of Demopolis. He stopped at noon to rest himself and the horse, taking a nap under a tree while Frank grazed nearby.

When he woke up, Frank was gone! Moses searched far and wide, but no horse. In desperation, he stopped at a neat white house to ask about his missing horse.

"No, sir, I haven't seen your horse," the homeowner, who happened to be a Methodist minister, replied. "But if you please to spend the night, tomorrow, which will be the Sabbath, I'll give notice in the meeting house, and perhaps something may come of it."

Accordingly, next morning the good man inquired from the pulpit whether any of his parishioners had seen a wandering black horse the previous day. To Moses' joyful surprise, a respectable-looking man stood up.

"I reckon I have him in my barn," he said. "A black horse strayed onto my place last night and I put him up till I could find out where he belonged. If the gentleman will come with me after meeting, he can have him."

Moses could have shouted for joy! The next day found him back at the Olivers', where his family had been anxiously waiting. They examined the wagon with various emotions and offered many comments and criticisms.

"I don't see where we are to sit," Betsey remarked as she studied the framework to which the wheels were attached.

"I think we might hold on," said Sally, "but then I don't know where the trunks would go. And together the girls walked around the creation, thoughtfully examining it from all sides. They were soon joined by numerous Negro children who were also curious about this strange-looking wagon.

Meanwhile, Martha and Moses stood together, talking things over. Mr. Oliver, drawn by curiosity, came out to join them.

"Of course," Moses explained with a smile, "this wagon is only the foundation. I shall have to make a body and concoct some kind of cover for it. The sun is hot and there might be rain."

"Are you going to try for some springs?" Mr. Oliver asked him.

"I'm afraid not," Mr. Royce replied. "I don't know enough about wagon building to attempt such a thing."

"No," laughed his wife, "and anyway, we have had so many hard knocks that what the wagon can do to us will seem like nothing at all."

Mr. Oliver, meantime, had been measuring the size of the framework. "I have an idea that I can help you with a bed for your wagon," he said. "My daughter's piano box should be just about right. It's a fine Chickering—the largest and best I could buy for her when she came back from finishing school in Mobile. I certainly was proud of her. She could play five pieces from memory."

"The box would be a great help to me if it should fit," Moses responded. "I'd be glad to pay you for it."

"Not at all," Mr. Oliver replied, glancing cautiously around to be sure his daughter was not within hearing. "I shall be happy to help out. You may have Joe to help fix things up. He works in my smithy and knows something about tools."

"Thank you, Mr. Oliver," Moses answered. "I'll get to work at once."

With Joe's assistance and much advice from Mr. Oliver, Moses worked diligently at assembling the piano box to the framework. At last, the odd vehicle began to look quite like the real thing. Once the Chickering box had been fitted on and firmly secured, flexible wooden bows were attached over it, to which a scanty muslin cover was secured. Martha was sorry they didn't have more muslin, but hoped it would be enough for shelter from rain and the hot sun.

Betsey and Sally paid careful attention to each step of the work and cheerfully ran errands for their father. Martha and Betsey went to work patching and darning the family's few clothes. Betsey had to smile when she remembered how she hated to sew when she was seven. She could hardly believe so much had happened since that day she threw the red thread on the woodpile. Now she liked to sew, especially since she made a dress for herself when she was eight years old. Of course, this happened at Walnut Hill, where there was a lot more material and a grandmother to encourage her.

Sally was not interested in sewing. She was happiest doing anything outdoors. Helping her father was much more to her taste than darning and patching under her mother's direction

"FATHER!" BETSEY EXCLAIMED.
"THOSE HORSES DON'T MATCH AT ALL!"

and watchful eye.

The remaining purchase was another horse to help Frank pull the wagon home to Franklin. Moses was directed to Mr. Travis on a neighboring plantation. There he purchased a small white mare named Patsy, which Mr. Travis said he had bought from a man of dubious background. Since the price was reasonable, Moses decided to take the risk and closed the deal.

The family questioned Moses' choice when small white Patsy was placed beside tall black Frank. The effect was so absurd that Sally burst into a fit of laughter. Even Martha could barely control her amusement. Betsey was the only one not amused. Her aesthetic sense was sadly jarred.

"Father!" she exclaimed. "Those horses don't match at ALL! Didn't you think of that when you bought Patsy?"

I'm afraid I didn't, my child," Moses replied. "I was mainly thinking of something with four good legs that could haul us home. And she does appear sturdy, doesn't she?"

That night, after the children were asleep, Martha and Moses talked over the details of their approaching journey. "The only things of value left to us are our two gold watches," said Martha. "I have been careful not to let them be seen since we came here. The slaves here were so very ignorant that they would think such trinkets immensely valuable. Would I do better to pack them on my person?"

"It's hard to say which," her husband replied. "I suppose you might hide one in a trunk and the other on your person, and so divide the risk. The rest of our belongings are so poor and scanty in any case that the meanest of thieves will not be attracted. We must be sure to dress as shabbily as possible."

"That's easy enough," Martha laughed. "Just as we stand will do."

"Now, about food," Moses went on, "We can buy some supplies from Mr. Travis since his household seems more thrifty. I've already bought a bag of flour, a small ham, a dozen eggs, and five pounds of honey. His wife has promised to boil the ham, have a batch of bread baked, and the eggs hard boiled. That will do to start us off. We have to trust to luck for other things along the way."

"Do you know," Martha remarked with eyes sparkling, "I believe I'm going to enjoy this journey more than any other I've made. I can see adventures all the way!"

"So can I," her husband answered quietly. There followed a pause, then the conversation continued. "Now, about camping along the way: I have my army blanket and you your long shawl. We can't all sleep in the wagon, but there'll be plenty of room outside. We could be very comfortable under the trees."

"Not I!" Martha stated emphatically. "I'm deathly afraid of snakes, and they always find me out. I am going to sleep in the wagon."

"Very well," Moses replied with a laugh, "You and one of the children, probably Sally, can sleep in the wagon, and Betsey and I will sleep under it. From there I'll be able to watch the horses during the night, since thieves are as plentiful as blackberries these days."

"How soon do you think we can start?" asked Martha.

Her husband considered for a few minutes. "This is Monday," he said. "I believe we can manage to leave by Wednesday. Tomorrow, I want to take the children to the brook for a last swim." Since Moses' return, he had given them several swimming lessons. Sally had done quite well, but Betsey had made little progress. The goal they hoped to reach before leaving the Oliver plantation was the ability to swim in what they called the "fathomless pool."

Tuesday was a busy day, with many things that had to be done before leaving the next morning. The two trunks and two old carpet bags were packed with their modest belongings. Mrs. Travis sent over the cooked food, together with the honey and flour. The children gave their homemade dolls and corncob carts to the little Negro children, who, on rare occasions, had been allowed to play with them.

A GENTEEL SPY

As the sun started to set, Moses called the children and headed to the brook for a last dip. Martha stayed behind to play the piano and sing "Lorena" and other mournful and sentimental songs of the day.

At the stream, they each went into the reeds and tall grasses to put on their worst clothes, which served as "bathing suits." Then their father began to give both girls a lesson in the proper strokes, taking them by turns into the deep pool.

"You don't seem to get on very fast, Betsey," he commented as he helped her out of the deeper pool to where it was safe and shallow. "I am going to take Sally in now, but you stay here and practice. See that you keep away from the deep hole."

Not knowing that she was even then standing on a large sunken rock at the very edge of that hole, Betsey stepped forward, determined to make a final effort to match Sally. In an instant, she recognized that she was in deep water. She did not struggle, but went straight down in an upright position. Her brain worked rapidly: *I have heard that people who drown sink and rise three times. This is my first sink, and when I come up to the top I will call out.* She held her breath until she felt herself rising, then, as her lips came to the surface, she screamed and sank again, still upright.

Moses looked hastily around. He saw her head bob up out of the water, then sink again out of sight. He stroked over quickly and pulled her out. As soon as both children were safely ashore he said, "Betsey, I'm afraid you'll never make a first class swimmer. Your talents don't seem to lie in that direction. Run along, now, both of you, and dress yourselves. We'll need a good night's rest before our journey tomorrow."

Wednesday dawned, clear and hot. The stagnant plantation

where so little of interest ever seemed to occur was quite stirred by the Royce's departure. Negroes of all ages hung around, sometimes assisting, but more often just looking on. The mismatched team Betsey had criticized stood at the gate, harnessed to the wagon, which was distinguished chiefly by the name "Chickering" in bold letters on either side. Mr. Oliver ordered hay brought to fill the wagon bed and added a small bag of ear corn for horse feed.

A thrill went through the crowd as the two trunks were carried out, one of ordinary size and the other a smaller "hat trunk." Next came well-worn carpet bags, the army blanket, Martha Royce's long shawl, and, finally, the Royces themselves. Martha had some trouble keeping the children's joy of leaving under control when they said good-bye to Mrs. Haley and Mr. Oliver.

Martha and Moses said all the proper and polite farewells. Mr. Oliver cordially wished them a successful journey and hoped he might hear from them upon their arrival in Tennessee. Mrs. Haley's handshake lacked warmth as her eyes rested on her piano box. "I'm afraid you are going to find that wagon bed very uncomfortable," she remarked. "I'm sure it's too small."

Somewhat chilled by Mrs. Haley's farewell, the family climbed into the wagon one by one and settled down.

"All right, Joe, bring along Dolly now," called Mr. Royce, and Joe came up with the plump little dapple-gray pony, which had been the children's greatest resource during the long, dull stay at the Oliver plantation. Her bridle reins were tied securely to the back of the wagon, the whip was cracked, and the team started forward. Dolly, however, pulled back with all her might when she saw the fluttering white wagon cover overhead! Since she was strong and well-fed, she proved more than a match for the lean team.

"Start her up, boys!" cried Mr. Oliver. With the assembled crowd shouting "Gid up! Gid up!" and rushing toward the pony, Dolly changed her mind and consented to trot behind the wagon as the team moved off once again.

Joy filled the hearts of the travelers as a bend in the road hid the cheerless place from their sight. They all felt that, no matter what lay before them, they were glad to take leave of that which lay behind!

Chapter Eleven
✤ Back To Franklin ✤

BETSEY AND SALLY WERE FEELING A LIGHTNESS OF SPIRIT now that they were finally on their way. They began to sing and hum whatever came to mind. Martha and Moses joined in with "Flow Gently Sweet Afton." Before "Sweet Afton" was finished, a sizable mud puddle appeared in their path. Moses let the horses feel their way through the deep puddle. All went well until the team started to climb the opposite bank. The temperamental pony, catching sight of the shaking white wagon cover, pulled backward hard. The team came to a sudden stop.

It was a deadlock until Moses, with muttered words and a ruffled temper, removed his shoes and socks, rolled up his trousers, and waded into the puddle. He untied the pony and led her onto dry land, where he tied her to a tree. Then he put on his shoes and drove the team out of the puddle. Meanwhile, not a sound was heard from the family.

"This pony is going to give us trouble all the way," Moses said crossly, "so I think we'd better sell her as soon as we can." At those words, both children burst into tears.

"Please don't sell Dolly, Father!" they cried together. "She'll be good, we know she will. Please don't, Father, she's all we have."

Moses and his wife exchanged glances. Then Martha said, "I

don't believe she is going to be led, but I have thought of something else. We have the tree of a man's saddle you brought back from Demopolis. If you can manage to strap that on Dolly's back, I will ride her. I don't think she'll give us any more trouble."

"But, Martha, that wouldn't be safe," Moses protested. "It's just a bare tree and I can only fasten it on with a leather strap."

"Never mind," Martha replied as she climbed down from the wagon. "I began riding when I was three and have ridden every kind of horse since. Everyone does in the bluegrass country. Bring out your old harness stuff. I'm sure that between us we can rig up a saddle."

When they had done as well as their limited resources would allow, Martha mounted the rebellious pony and the journey continued. The children kept an anxious watch on Dolly and her rider.

An hour later, Moses stopped the wagon and Martha drew alongside. "It's almost noon," he said as he looked at the sun, "and we are quite near the Black Warrior River. I think it's about another mile. Suppose we push on and have our dinner there. There is a good spring nearby and the ferry is only a half a mile or so."

"That sounds fine," Martha replied. "I am getting hungry."

"So are we," cried the two little girls, "and Mrs. Travis' biscuits do look good."

In a short time they had reached the Black Warrior, which proved to be a perfect picnic spot. Dense foliage shaded the family from the hot sun, with ample water for the horses and humans alike. It would have been tempting to spend the afternoon in such a restful place, but they had a ferry to catch.

BACK TO FRANKLIN

After they were ferried across the river, they reached Eutaw, where they would spend the night. In a country so unsettled and lawless, Moses felt they would be safer staying close to a town or large plantation. As they entered Eutaw, they were aware of being watched closely by a well-dressed gentleman. He seemed especially interested in the white mare.

Finally, he approached Moses. "Where did you get that mare you're driving?"

"I bought her from Mr. Travis," Moses replied.

"What did you pay for her?" the man asked.

"Forty dollars," Moses said.

"Well, she's mine!" the stranger answered. "She was stolen from me at a picnic, and I haven't seen her since. Where are you headed?"

Moses decided to throw himself on the man's mercy. He told him of the family's refugee life, their present destination, and their effort to return to their home and friends.

In response, the stranger said kindly, "I see your situation, and I won't stop you. As it happens, I know Mr. Travis and we will settle it between us. I think he will do what's right." So saying, he wished them a safe journey and rode away.

"A good fellow," said Moses as he heaved a sigh of relief. "Had he reclaimed his horse, which he had every right to do, I might have been forced to turn horse thief myself! It seems a popular profession now."

"Not surprising," Martha remarked, "in such times as these."

The Royces drove to the far side of town and stopped for the night in a small grove. The horses were fed and tethered near the wagon, and then the family ate.

"If only I had a cup of good hot coffee," Martha sighed, "I think I would die happy. I wonder if I shall ever taste it again."

"That is just a delicious dream at present," Moses replied, "but someday it may come true. I haven't tasted it myself since I escaped from prison." Coffee was not the only scarce food supply. Bakery bread was seldom found, so the Royces bought flour; and if they were lucky they found a woman willing to bake biscuits for them. It was summer, so fresh fruit took the place of vegetables.

The family kept a steady pace toward Aberdeen, making the food they could find last as long as possible. Martha was looking forward to spending a few days visiting a cousin who lived not far from Aberdeen.

"Mother," said Sally, "I sure hope your cousin, Erasmus, has something good for us to eat. I'm so tired of being hungry!"

"We will have to wait and see," said her mother, "and you must not ask about food, Sally. You will have to wait and see what they serve."

"Yes, Mother, I'll try. But it won't be easy."

Betsey and Sally took turns riding Dolly to make the time go faster. Finally, they pulled up in front of cousin Erasmus' gate. They were greeted warmly by Erasmus and his wife, Abby. The Royces were shown to a guest house, where they went to work cleaning up for supper.

Once they were seated, plates of piping hot fried chicken were brought to the table, and all four Royces couldn't have been happier. Sally gave a scream of delight as the chicken was passed.

Martha, who felt like doing the same thing, could scold her only a little. When a pot of genuine coffee was placed before Martha, she and Moses smiled broadly.

"This is especially in your honor," Abby said. "Erasmus found it in Aberdeen yesterday, just in time for your visit. I hope we'll be able to buy it regularly from now on."

"I cannot tell you what a treat this is for us, Abby," Martha responded. "Just the other night, Moses and I were talking about how much we missed real coffee. There is nothing so good."

"Oh, yes there is," Sally piped up. "It's fried chicken!" Everyone laughed, and the dinner hour passed pleasantly.

The visit with Abby and Erasmus Broyles was just what the Royces needed to renew their energy for the remainder of the trip. Their clothes were laundered, food supplies replenished, and horses rested. Betsey couldn't help thinking what a difference it was from the Oliver plantation.

Once they were on their way, Sally asked to be first riding Dolly. She was told to stay behind the wagon in order for Martha to keep an eye on her and Dolly. This worked well until they came down a steep hill and Dolly caught sight of the shawl under the saddle, which was hanging loose on one side. It was all she needed to bolt—a runaway completely out of control. Sally barely held onto the saddle horn.

Martha screamed to Moses, "Jump out and stop the pony!" Moses jumped in front of Dolly and threw up his arms, which stopped her so abruptly that she reared straight up, throwing Sally onto the ground under her. As Dolly's hoof came down straight toward Sally's head, neither Martha nor Betsey could bear to watch. They could only hold onto each other, shutting out the expected sight of Sally's death. The next thing they heard was Moses' groan and Sally's scream. Then the clatter of hooves as Dolly galloped into the woods.

Moses picked Sally up. She was crying hysterically. When she was able to talk, she told her anxious family that Dolly had stepped on her side. Upon examination they found that she was more scared then hurt.

"The Lord was with us, Martha," her husband said with a tremor in his voice.

Martha held Sally in her arms and said quietly, "We have much for which to be thankful."

Dolly could be heard in the thicket, plunging, rearing, and kicking. She finally came out on the road and stood trembling, waiting for attention. The saddle and blanket had been kicked off, and her foreleg was cut and bleeding.

Moses looked her over and said, "I think we are having too much pony on this trip. We had better sell her this time, the first chance we get."

As before, the girls cried and begged for their pony. For all of Dolly's faults, she was the one thing they could call their own. And except for the times when she was spooked, riding Dolly was the only fun Sally and Betsey had in their lives. Since there was no buyer in sight, the decision regarding Dolly was put off. The girls breathed a sigh of relief, and Betsey whispered in Dolly's ear to "please be good."

It seemed as if Dolly had no sooner recovered from the cut on her leg when they had another horse problem. Frank, the big black horse who was so dependable on the level road, wanted to go downhill at a fast trot. With the countryside becoming more

BACK TO FRANKLIN

AS DOLLY'S HOOF CAME DOWN
STRAIGHT TOWARDS SALLY'S HEAD, NEITHER
MOTHER NOR BETSEY COULD BEAR TO WATCH.

hilly, Moses had all he could do to control his team. It was obvious that in Frank's previous life he had a different kind of bit, because the single bit had little or no effect on him.

At one hill there were two men halfway down, walking their horse carefully over a rough section. Away went Frank, with Moses leaning back on the reins and everything in the wagon bouncing up as high as it could. Everyone held tight as they flew past the men, who had drawn their horse to one side when they saw Frank coming.

When Moses finally brought Frank under control on level ground, the men came up to speak to him.

"That is a very dangerous horse you are driving, stranger," said one of them, "and if you don't mind, I feel he will be the cause of an accident."

"I am obliged to you for the warning," Moses answered when he had recovered his breath. "I would be pleased to travel slower if I could." The men laughed at his answer and wished him Godspeed. Fortunately for the Royces, the road leveled off and Frank became dependable once more.

The countryside through which they traveled was left desolate by armies. For ten miles at a stretch, they passed nothing but deserted houses. The doors were open and the Royces saw furniture inside. Sally asked her father why the people left their furniture in their houses. "They had to leave quickly, Sally, to get away from the fighting," Moses explained.

Betsey looked at her little sister. "Don't you remember, Sally, how Mother had to sell our furniture before we left Franklin?"

"I guess so," Sally answered, "but I was too sad about leaving Charlie Cat to remember anything else."

BACK TO FRANKLIN

By now it was the middle of August and intensely hot. The family and the horses felt the heat, and they made slow progress. They finally reached the Latrobe plantation, their first stop after leaving Erasmus Broyles. The plantation was so large that they traveled a mile through cotton fields before they came to the site Moses had in mind for their camp.

The sun was setting as a weary Moses unhitched the horses and led them away to water. Betsey and Sally climbed down from the wagon, happy to stretch their legs. Martha stayed in the wagon, partly from weariness and partly from a growing sense of uneasiness. The place seemed to her much too remote and lonely to be safe.

Suddenly, and seemingly from nowhere, four or five Negro women appeared, uncouth-looking and half-clad. After staring hard at the wagon for what seemed to Martha like a very, very long time, they gathered around the little girls and began talking to them in a language Betsey and Sally could hardly understand. They finally understood what the women wanted when they took their hands and looked closely at the tiny gold rings they were wearing.

"Gol'! Dese am gold," one exclaimed, and the others took up the word and passed it from one to another. All the time, the number of former slaves kept increasing. Now and then, one would run away from the growing circle and return with more.

Betsey and Sally held fast to each other, keeping close to the wagon where their mother sat. The same two women came up to the girls again, and this time one of them took Sally by her ring hand. "Come 'long wid me to de peach o'chad, missy," she said, "an I'll give you some nice ones."

Sally pulled her hand away and ran from the woman. Betsey followed close behind, and they both scrambled up into the wagon and snuggled close to their mother. At once, several women came up and peered in, noting the wedding ring on Martha's hand and the baggage. They looked especially hard at the two trunks, which seemed large enough to hold vast treasures.

Though she was a plucky woman, Martha was cold with fear. *What has become of Moses? Why is he so long in coming? What if they have attacked him?* Such troubling thoughts flashed through her brain as she and the children huddled together, praying for help.

Martha thought how different the Negroes who surrounded the wagon were from the dear familiar faces at Walnut Hill. It seemed to her that these were little better than savages, with no one to hold them in check. *They think our baggage is so valuable that they are planning to murder us.* Her thoughts ran on and on in this desperate vein.

From the wagon, Martha could see an ever-increasing crowd of women, children, and young boys, all laughing, singing, dancing and sometimes even rolling and kicking half-naked in the sand. The women had been uttering long, piercing calls for some time, and now, in response, men began to appear from the cotton fields.

I fear our time is near and poor Moses is gone, Martha thought, and prayed again for help.

Little Sally, with tears running down her cheeks, murmured, "Now I lay me down to sleep."

Betsey, tense with fear, prayed silently, her eyes fastened on the road along which her father, if alive, would return.

Every now and then, the family heard loud calls for "Zeke," whom the crowd seemed to be waiting for. Once Martha heard someone say "Dere ain't no white folks on dis place no mo."

Suddenly, Betsey's face brightened. "Mother," she whispered, "Father is coming!" Peeking out anxiously through the semi-darkness, the family saw Moses leading the three horses along slowly, evidently unaware of the threatening crowd. When he reached the wagon and saw his family sitting inside, he looked surprised.

"Why don't you get out and have your supper?" he asked. "The sun has set."

Quickly Martha whispered back, "Moses, look around. We haven't a moment to lose. We must hitch up and make our escape at once or we shall all be killed. I can't tell you more now—just that we must go *at once!*"

Moses glanced around and understood instantly. He began to harness the weary horses. "Betsey, you will have to ride Dolly, and the rest of us will go in the wagon until we are free of the crowd. Then we shall all have to walk. The horses are so tired I'm afraid they will drop from exhaustion."

The crowd surrounding them did not seem to sense what was going on until the wagon began to move. "Where you goin'? What you goin' to do?" they cried in tones of surprise.

"I'm going on a little ways," Moses replied as matter-of-factly as he could, "to where there's a better camping place."

The crowd seemed uncertain, as though their plan had been upset. Then a group started to follow the wagon and was soon joined by others. The numbers increased as the family passed through the great plantation on their way out to the main road.

It was dark, except for the moonlight. Moses stopped the wagon, dismounted, and helped his wife and daughters out of the wagon.

"We must all walk and walk as fast as we can to lighten the load. The horses are on the edge of failing us, and the Negroes are close behind. They will soon overtake us if we don't hurry on. Betsey is alright on the pony, but look out for Sally, Martha, or she may give out."

"I won't give out; I won't give out," protested little Sally. She ran along at her mother's side, holding her hand tightly. "Don't talk, Sally dear," her mother cautioned. "Save your breath." Silence fell, and only the sound of their labored breathing and the hoof beats of the horses could be heard.

Sometimes the group giving chase seemed to be very close, and Martha shuddered when she thought of a stranger's hand reaching out to grab her or her little girls. A terrible thought passed her mind: *If we should be murdered here, no one would ever know what had become of us. We would vanish as completely as if the earth swallowed us up!*

Moses prayed for the safety of his family with each mile the exhausted horses covered. He thought of the wagon as it rocked and swayed, and had to trust in the Lord that the wagon would not turn over or the rotten harness break.

By this time, they had reached the public road, which passed through a dense forest. The way was dark, brightened only by patches of moonlight. The pine trees sighed in the wind, and strange sounds could be heard, mixed with human shouts and calls. The most alarming was the muted sound of feet running through the sand.

At long last, they left the woods behind them. Now the road

lay between open fields, and in the distance they could see lights.

"That must be Somerset," Moses remarked, speaking for the first time and gradually slowing down. The sounds of the chase grew fainter, and finally stopped altogether. With cries of joy, the Royces embraced one another, their fears at an end.

"That was a very close call," said Martha. "I pray we will never have another so frightening."

"May I ride in the wagon the rest of the way?" little Sally asked. "My legs are real tired."

"You certainly may," replied her father as he lifted her in. "You have been a plucky little girl. Now we can walk slowly the rest of the way. I don't think it is more than half a mile to the village."

"I'm really starved," wailed Sally, whose appetite was always strong, no matter what was happening.

"So are we all," agreed Martha, suddenly realizing how long it had been since their last meal. They all sat down by an old mill and opened the basket of food that Abby had packed for them. The day ended with peace and contentment as they all lay down to sleep.

When Moses woke up the next morning, he felt someone standing quite close to him. Looking out from under the wagon, where he always slept, he saw a short, stout man. Quickly Moses scrambled out from under his blanket.

"Good morning, sir," he said to the man, who seemed to be the miller.

"Good morning, stranger," replied the miller. "Where did you come from, if I may be so bold to ask?"

"You certainly may," replied Moses. "We came from Aberdeen yesterday morning, but came here last night in a desperate hurry. We had stopped at the Latrobe plantation, where we planned to camp."

The miller raised his eyebrows and gave a slow whistle. "That shows you're a stranger, if you planned to camp there," he said. "You'd never have seen daylight if you had. Mrs. Latrobe is seldom there now, and the overseers have left. Those Negroes are the same as a jungle tribe. They know they're free and they're crazy mad. In fact, white folks around here are none too safe outside the towns. Where are you folks heading?"

Moses told him their final destination was Franklin, Tennessee. He asked how far to Fulton, the nearest town. The miller explained there were two ways to go. Their safest route was thirty miles. He told Moses the other route cut off eight miles but was hazardous with fallen trees. He had also heard there were robbers all along the way.

Moses and Martha talked it over and decided on the shorter route. They felt the road would be cleared by now, and since their clothes were so shabby, they would not attract robbers. The only thing of any value was the pony, and they could take a chance on her.

"Oh, I will ride Dolly," Betsey said with confidence.

"Very well," Moses nodded, smiling, "we'll turn her over to you."

Betsey took on her responsibility very seriously.

The Royces started out on the shorter road, which soon became very rough. The springless wagon bounced along so painfully that Martha and Sally would get off and walk every little while. This also eased the job for the horses. They stopped to eat beside a brook, and Betsey said to the others, "We haven't seen a single robber yet."

"All's gone well so far," Moses cautioned, "but it's still too early to do much boasting."

All at once, at a sharp bend in the road, they came upon a luxurious patch of green grass, the first they had seen since their trip began. Eagerly, the pony turned toward it, and Betsey loosened the reins to let her eat. She thought there couldn't be any harm in letting poor hungry Dolly have one little nibble, and the wagon was just ahead.

At that moment came a clatter of hooves and the sound of men's voices. Suddenly, from nowhere, appeared four men on horseback, leading two other horses.

Betsey's heart gave a leap, for she knew at once that she was facing a band of robbers. Pulling up Dolly's reins, she sat quietly looking at the men. They all seemed surprised at the sight of a little girl on horseback. Betsey nudged the pony on, conscious that the men were watching her. As she passed them, she heard one of them say, "That's a very good little horse, Jacko."

Betsey went on as fast as she could until she saw her father coming to meet her as she turned a bend in the road. Martha and Sally were standing by the wagon, anxiously waiting for her.

"Betsey," her father said with unusual sternness, "you must not fall so far behind—it isn't safe. Those men who just passed us were very likely robbers."

For another mile or two, the family traveled on in silence. Then they saw a cluster of houses ahead. "I'm sure that must be

Fulton," Moses said with a sigh of relief. "No more short cuts for me," as they hit another bump.

Martha emphatically agreed.

Only fire-scorched chimneys marked where houses once stood. Fences had vanished, forests cut down. Here and there, the remains of an army camp could be seen. At noon, they stopped to have lunch beside an empty house with a good spring nearby. Martha and the girls couldn't resist going into the old house to look around. Only the heavier pieces of furniture remained. The lighter ones had been carted off by thieves.

"The owners must have left in a hurry," Martha observed as she surveyed the scene. "Cooking pots are on the stove and the kitchen table, as if the family had been in the midst of preparing a meal."

Just then a lean and hungry-looking cat emerged from under the house. It looked at them nervously, mewing all the time.

"Oh, please mother, let me give her a piece of bread," Sally pleaded.

"Make it half a piece," her mother replied grimly, "or you may end up mewing yourself." Sally looked very serious as she held out a bit of bread to the starving cat.

"Look, Mother, at what I found." Betsey came running with a rattle and a baby's bib. "There must have been a baby in the family."

"We have seen enough," Martha observed, a pained expression on her face. "Come, let's have our lunch." As they all went out, she carefully closed the door behind her—though why, she could not have said.

After lunch, Martha and Moses sat and talked while the girls did more exploring. "This is the most depressing country I have ever seen," Martha said, "although I've said nothing about it to the children. I saw something of war in the two years before we were ordered out of Franklin and became refugees. But since we stayed out of the path of the armies and actual battles, we have been spared such devastation. It is heart-rending and makes me understand that biblical passage: 'by the waters of Babylon we sat down and wept...' in a new way. Those words have been running through my mind all day."

"There, there, Martha dear," her husband replied sympathetically, "you have been very courageous all along and mustn't lose heart now. The South played for big stakes and lost. Now we must all do our part to pay up. I don't wonder you are saddened and depressed by this countryside, but further along it gets better. War itself is stimulating and exciting for the duration; it's the aftermath that costs."

"Yes, that is true," Martha agreed, her face brightening as memories came back. "In those years in Franklin after you joined the army, the children and I had very few dull moments. Van Dorn's attack on the town was exciting, certainly, even though we had to hide in the cellar for protection from the Minies that rained through the house. That episode was 'stimulating' to say the least."

Then Moses took his turn to reminisce. "I think the greatest thrill the war brought me was my escape from the military prison in Nashville — on the oddest night of the year, February 29. We certainly 'leaped' out of that cell! I haven't known such excitement since."

Just then, the children returned. Their parents, feeling more cheerful for their talk, got up and prepared to move on.

"That kitty won't make friends with me at all," complained Sally, a devoted cat lover. "And she reminds me so much of Charlie Cat."

"How can you say that?" Betsey frowned. "This cat is gray and Charlie was yellow and white." Sally did not answer, but Betsey could tell she was unconvinced.

After a thankfully uneventful journey, the Royces reached Florence as the sun was setting. They crossed the Tennessee River, admiring the beautiful sunset colors reflected in the water. They were still caught in the beauty of the scene when a man's angry voice shattered the peaceful moment.

They were passing a livery stable on the outskirts of town, and they could hear him saying emphatically, "That's my horse and I'm going after her!" His eyes fixated on Dolly, and he carried on a heated exchange with several men who had gathered at the stable door.

Moses hurried his tattered team along while Betsey, on the pony, stayed very close to the wagon. They turned a street corner and were soon out of town. Although they heard no one chasing them, Moses quickly turned off the main road and into a grove of sheltering trees.

"That was another close call, Moses," said his wife. "I'm sure the man meant Dolly, for that mark on her face cannot be mistaken. I have always been afraid it would give her away."

Moses began to laugh. "Do you know," he remarked, "we are all getting demoralized and soon will be no better than the other horse thieves! I paid very little for her and the man who sold her to me seemed in a hurry to get his money and leave. In any case, she's mine now and I'm going to keep her."

Martha had to suppress a smile, remembering several occasions on the trip when Moses would have gladly sold Dolly on the spot. That night, Moses and Martha took turns sitting up and guarding Dolly until daylight came. Betsey wanted to help, so she took watch with her father for the early part of the night. She shared his blanket while gazing at the brilliant stars until night overcame her and she fell asleep.

The next morning, the family made an unusually early start, partly to avoid the heat and partly to escape a possible chase. It seemed the latter was less of a threat, for which they were all grateful.

Within an hour or so they had crossed the Tennessee line. All felt cheered to know they were back on home territory. To Sally and Betsey the country was all new. But their parents soon began to recognize familiar places, even though the hand of war had fallen heavily on all of them. Moses noticed that they were not far from Mt. Pleasant. "Do you remember the Polk family who live nearby, Martha?"

"Yes, indeed, I do," replied Martha, "When you taught at Columbia, one of your students was William Polk. I remember his parents' kindness to you and being invited to their home after we were married. They are indeed an aristocratic family. Their handsome home was one I will always remember."

"Would you like to stop for a moment and say 'how do you do' as we pass by?" Moses asked. "I'm sure they would be glad to see us."

"Heavens, no!" Martha cried, aghast at the idea. "Think how we look! Your skin is showing through the knee of your trouser leg, and just look at us." The little girls giggled.

"Very well," Moses agreed. But being a man unembarrassed by his outward appearance, as well as a warm friend of the distinguished Polks, he was slightly disappointed.

For another hour or so they pushed on in silence, until a young man on horseback came cantering down the road. As he drew near, they noticed the superior beauty of the horse he rode. The young man slowed down, looked at Moses intently, then stopped beside the wagon. Moses did the same, all the time focusing on the rider.

Suddenly, from both men burst a glad cry of recognition. Moses jumped down from the wagon as the young man threw himself off his mount. They greeted each other warmly.

"To think of meeting you here, Mr. Royce!" the young man exclaimed as they shook hands. "I can't tell you how pleased I am."

"And I was just thinking of you, William my boy," replied Moses, "for I knew we were not far from your place. Indeed I was hoping..." Here he checked himself, mindful of his wife. "Come and meet my wife and two little girls. You remember Mr. Polk, Martha, I am sure."

After polite greetings had been exchanged all around, Mr. Polk invited them to spend the night at their home. When this did not seem possible, they were urged to have dinner with his family. Moses and Martha found many reasons why, regretfully, they must decline. The young man seemed so disappointed that they compromised by agreeing to stop for a short visit at the house.

"I am sorry not to see more of you," declared the young man, "but half a loaf is better than no bread at all." And, bowing, he mounted his horse and cantered away.

"I should have liked nothing better than to have stayed overnight with those delightful people," Martha sighed, "but I just couldn't when we looked like such tramps. Suppose we pull off into the woods and tidy up as best we can so at least we'll be clean."

So they turned into the woods and opened their trunks, doing what they could to make themselves presentable. The pony was tied to the back of the wagon so that Betsey need not rumple her clean dress with riding. Their cleaning up completed, the family got back in the wagon and soon drew up before the Polk's stately mansion.

The house, built of brick, was large and imposing; two stories with a high basement and a roof with several dormer windows. A tall pillared porch and a long flight of steps lent dignity to the entrance. Immediately in front of the house, a high iron gate of Italian design opened into the grounds. While the beautiful trees appeared to have come through the war undamaged, the flower garden showed neglect. A statue which once adorned the end of a long walk now lay across the path, prostrate and broken.

Just as the Royces drew up in front of the house, the door opened and William, along with his parents, hurried down the steps to greet them warmly. The Polks represented all that was best about Southern aristocracy before the war. They were simple, dignified, well-educated, and extremely hospitable. They were never content to rest on their heritage and loyally served both church and state. Once greetings were exchanged, the Polks urged their visitors to come into the house.

"We would be delighted to do so," Moses answered for his family, "but we must not yield to temptation. The sun is sinking lower every minute and we must make Laurel before nightfall."

"Then we will talk outdoors all we can," Mrs. Polk replied. Chairs were brought and everyone seated himself under the trees. In a few moments, a Negro butler appeared, carrying on a large silver tray the standard refreshments served in the South: pound cake and wine. Ever hungry, the Royces accepted with pleasure. Sally most of all, though the wine brought tears to her eyes.

The butler's hair was white, his livery worn and faded; but his manner reflected the attentiveness and dignified self-respect typical of a slave born and raised in the house he served. When he had withdrawn, Moses remarked to his host, "I am so pleased to see that Pompey is still with you; so many slaves left as soon as they knew they were free."

"Not he," replied Mr. Polk. "I think Pompey will remain with us always. In fact, there is a strong attachment on both sides. He has lived all his life in this house, and we scarcely ever think of him as a slave."

Just then, William joined them. "I've been thinking about the pony you have with you," he said. "If you don't need her, why not leave her with us? Horse thieves are numerous in these parts. Even discharged soldiers will steal horses to get back home or use for working in the fields. We have a strong stockade where she will be safe till you send for her."

"A good plan, William," agreed his father. "We'd be delighted to help you in that or any other way."

"Thank you for your kindness," Moses replied. "I shall be only too glad to accept your offer, for we certainly have no need of her now." So Dolly was deleted from the pilgrim's company, to the great relief of all.

Mrs. Polk, Martha, and the children joined the men. "This has been delightful and most restful," said Martha. "Mrs. Polk and I have talked of many things. But now we really must be on our way."

After Dolly had been untied and led away, and warm farewells exchanged, the Royces continued on their journey. Betsey looked back as long as she could, until the Polk mansion was hidden from view. *How I would enjoy living in a place like that*, she thought, but knew enough to keep such thoughts to herself.

The next day, they traveled through a section of country that had had such a long drought that many wells and springs had dried up. The houses where they stopped for water could only allow drinks for themselves, none for the horses. It was not until late afternoon, just a few miles from Columbia, that they finally found a small stream. At last, the suffering horses could drink freely.

Soon afterward, they entered the outskirts of the town, where they had to cross a dilapidated wooden bridge spanning a deep railroad cut. The railings of the bridge were rotten, in some places missing altogether. Occasional holes showed in the floor with signs of more to follow. The Royces were on the bridge, the appearance of which filled them with a sense of foreboding.

Suddenly, Moses called out, "What makes this horse act so strangely?" Frank, the tall black, was headed straight for the edge of the bridge where the railing was broken down. Moses found himself powerless to hold or guide him. Another step would take him over the edge, dragging the small white horse and the wagon down to the railroad track forty feet below!

"Jump! Jump!" cried Martha. And the whole family, including Moses, who hastily dropped the reins, leapt from the wagon. They fell sprawling onto the bridge floor without a second to spare. Slowly they got to their feet, dreading to see a big gap where the horses and wagon had been just a moment before.

But, to their amazement, the wagon and the small white horse were standing near the edge of the bridge. Frank's last step had been through a hole in the floor. Mercifully, he had fallen inward rather than outward. Just one step lay between safety and destruction, and the horse had blindly chosen the first. Now he was lying stiff and rigid on the bridge floor, a victim of what might be called a "fit".

While the girls looked on, stunned by the accident, Moses loosened the harness on the fallen horse. Martha hurried to the far end of the bridge, where several Union soldiers could be seen at the toll house. When she asked for help, they came quickly and soon revived Frank. He staggered to his feet, still looking dazed.

"Has he ever had a fit like this before?" one of the men inquired.

"Not since I've owned him," Moses replied. "But since the country is very dry, I was unable to water them till shortly before we got here. Frank drank a great deal, but so did the other horse, which makes me wonder if that was the cause."

"Undoubtedly it was," returned the soldier. "Nothing is worse for a horse than a big drink when he is hot and tired. But he seems to be alright now. We'll harness him up and see you over the bridge. I don't think he'll give you any more trouble — not for a while anyway," he added.

And so the friendly enemy escorted the family over the rotten bridge and wished them Godspeed into Columbia.

"The guardian angel was close at hand that time," Martha commented soberly. "It was a question of whether the horse would fall to the right or to the left, and he happened to fall to the right."

"You guessed correctly," Moses replied, "when you said before we started that our journey would be full of adventures."

"Nevertheless," Martha came back with spirit, "I *have* enjoyed it more than any other journey I ever made." At this, Moses remained silent.

"Suppose the wagon and team had gone over the bridge," Betsey said aloud after much thinking, "We would have had to walk the rest of the way to Franklin, wouldn't we?"

"Yes," added Sally, "and maybe beg our food as we went along." *I wouldn't mind so much doing that*, she thought.

Fortunately, Sally did not have to beg for food. Moses saw the headmaster of the Columbia Institute, where he once had taught Latin, coming down the street. There was a joyful reunion, and Dr. Payne and his wife insisted that they spend the night at the Institute, since the students were gone and there was plenty of room.

The weary travelers accepted gratefully and spent a comfortable night at the school. By the following afternoon they were nearing Franklin at last. They had maintained a slow pace out of consideration for Frank. They did not wish to have a repetition of their experience on the bridge.

"If he will only hold out till we reach Franklin," Moses said, half holding his breath and half praying, "I'm sure we can manage the rest some way."

Nodding her agreement, Martha remarked thoughtfully, "We are returning by the same road on which the girls and I first went out two years ago. The Cloustons, who with ourselves were the first families ordered out, returned after a time, but we have been long on the road." Then, after a short pause, she exclaimed, "There on the right is the house where we stopped to see General Van Dorn. We can't be far from home now."

"Was General Van Dorn that handsome man with the long gold chain around his waist?" Betsey asked with interest.

"Yes," replied Martha, "only I don't believe the chain was really around his waist." Sally confessed that she had forgotten him entirely. They were within one short mile of Franklin as the sun drew near to setting. "We can just about make it, I think," Moses was saying hopefully, when to his dismay Frank began to pull hard on the reins. Walking stiffly off one side of the road, he fell down in a heap. He revived shortly and was able to stand up again, weak and trembling.

Nothing remained but for the travelers to swallow their disappointment, unharness the team and make one last encampment within sound—and almost within sight—of their goal. Despite their discomfort and frustration, one glad thought sustained them: They had reached the end of the trail!!

Chapter Twelve
❧ Beginning Again ❧

NEXT MORNING, THE ROYCES WOKE UP EARLY after a restless night. They used the last of their provisions for breakfast, with water from a house half a mile away. The water was given sparingly, with none for the horses due to the continuing drought.

From over the hill came the sounds of the waking town. The family felt cheered by the barking of dogs, crowing of roosters, and the whistling of a departing train.

"We mustn't come in too soon or the poor Cloustons won't be ready to see us," Martha cautioned. "They've been dear friends for so many years, I know they'll give us a warm welcome. I can hardly wait to see them."

"Very well," Moses replied, "we shall wait a while. In the meantime, I'll tidy up the wagon and throw out anything we don't need."

Betsey began to laugh. "I didn't know there was anything we didn't need, Father," she said. "Let me see what you mean."

Both girls ran over to the wagon and helped their father toss out the remnants of the hay and fodder, which, throughout the long trip, was food for the horses and bedding for them.

"That does look better," Martha commented, peering in. "Now it's my turn. I shall put the trunk in order. We must each put on a clean dress, girls," she went on, handing the children their clothes, "and here is a fresh shirt for you, Moses. I wish I could give you clean trousers, but as you are wearing your last pair, you'll just have to make them do."

The sun was up by the time they were ready. More and more people began to pass along the Columbia turnpike. "Now we are off," Moses said at last. "I only hope Frank will stay on his feet for a little longer."

After climbing the low hill, they stopped for a few moments to enjoy their first view of the place they had worked so hard to reach. Before the war, Franklin had been called one of the prettiest towns in the state. Even from a distance, the Royces could now see evidence of many changes. Trees which once had lined the streets were missing, and fences were gone. A fort had been built on the opposite bank of the Harpeth River. Running across Carter's field was a long line of breastworks with corresponding ditches.

Saying nothing to the children, Moses and his wife glanced across the wide field to the spot where their house had stood. "It's all downhill to the town now," Moses remarked with a forced cheerfulness, "so if we can hurry up we'll soon be there." Gently snapping the reins, he drove past Carter's battle-scarred brick house and into town. A few minutes later, they drew up before the Clouston home, which was a small but comfortable house on one of the side streets.

"Run in, girls, and see if they know you." Martha said. Betsey and Sally happily jumped down and ran to knock on the door. In a moment, it was opened by the warm-hearted Louise Clouston, their mother's dearest friend and Betsey's godmother. Silently, the children gazed at her and she at them. Suddenly her puzzled expression gave way to recognition.

"You little dears! Wherever did you come from?" she cried, kissing them each in turn. Calling to her mother and sisters that "the Royces are here!," she ran down the walk to greet Martha and Moses.

Once the initial exuberance of reunion had subsided, the two families went into the house. Mrs. Clouston, along with her daughters, insisted the Royces stay with them while they made plans for starting over.

"We'll find room for you all if you don't mind squeezing up a bit," Mrs. Clouston assured them.

"'Squeezing up a bit!'" Martha cried with a laugh. "Did you hear that, Moses? 'Squeezing up a bit' after three weeks of sleeping in a piano box!"

"You dear people are the soul of kindness," Moses responded feelingly. "Since we are absolutely homeless, we are only too glad to accept the shelter of your roof for a time." He turned hastily and went out.

After the mid-day dinner, Martha suggested that they walk out and see where their house had stood. However, Louise discouraged her.

"Wait till tomorrow," she urged kindly. "Once you've had a good night's rest, we can go out there." Martha accepted this advice, for in her heart of hearts she dreaded seeing the spot again, as one might shrink from looking on the face of the dead.

While his family was resting, Moses walked uptown, wondering how many residents were left whom he had known. He was surprised to find more than he expected. Sadly, he heard of the good friends who had died in the bloody battle of Franklin the year before. Among the old friends he was especially happy to see was Nicholas Perkins. He was once a prosperous land-owner living five miles outside of Franklin.

"I am glad to welcome you back, Royce," he said as they shook hands cordially. "Where are you and the family staying?"

"With the Cloustons," Moses replied.

"Yes, yes, very good," Nicholas said, but Moses saw him cast-ing a sidelong glance at a well-dressed stranger who appeared to be watching them. In a lower voice Perkins warned, "Keep off the streets and out of sight as much as you can. I'll explain later." Then, "I shall see you tomorrow," he concluded in a louder and cheerful voice. So saying, he smiled at Moses and went on his way.

Following a refreshing night's sleep, Martha again proposed that the family walk out to the site of their former home. Moses declined, however, preferring to remain at the Clouston's to wait for Nicholas Perkins' visit. Moses also felt that he would rather contemplate the disaster of his former home alone, instead of with his sorrowful family.

Since Louise Clouston was a true and faithful friend, she went with Martha and the girls to do what she could to keep their spirits up. The girls walked on ahead, with Sally indulging in talk of how the house would look and whether the soldiers had cut down their crabapple tree. She even entertained the thought that Charlie Cat might still be wandering around. Sally, had, of course, been told that the house was destroyed by the Yankees, but her imagination would not let her accept that fact.

Betsey remained quiet. She acknowledged what she knew to

be the truth when she looked across Carter's field the day before. As the party passed by the large brick house where their good friends the McNutts had lived, it looked quiet and empty. Louise explained to Martha that the McNutts had become refugees several months after the Royces left. Betsey was listening to their conversation and she couldn't help interrupting:

"What happened to grandmother's portrait? Oh, please don't tell me the Yankees got it. Mr. McNutt said he would take care of it and Father's books."

"It's alright, Betsey, I didn't have time to tell you," Louise said, smiling at her godchild. "We have the portraits. The McNutts knew we were good friends and would take care of them till you came home. Mr. Perkins offered to keep your father's books, so they are safe as well."

Sally, finally aware of what they were talking about, piped up with, "What about Charlie Cat? Who has my Charlie Cat?"

Louise and Martha exchanged glances and unspoken words. Finally, Louise pulled Sally to her, knelt down, and spoke softly: "When Alice McNutt had to leave, she found a wonderful new home for your kitty. Charlie Cat is living on a farm near Nashville, where he gets plenty of food and a lot of love from his new family. I know they are hoping you will let him stay with them."

Sally was quiet for a while. Finally, she looked at her mother and "Aunt" Louise and said with a brave smile, "I guess he can stay there. I'm glad he has plenty to eat. I wouldn't want him to be hungry like we were. But I still want another Charlie Cat and I don't want to ever give it away!" Her mother smiled and gave Sally an extra-big hug. So did "Aunt" Louise.

At last they reached the place they'd been seeking. They

stopped and looked around. Louise tactfully remained silent while the family gazed upon a scene of blank desolation such as they were never to forget. The pretty little house that had been their home had vanished like a dream. So had the flowers, the shrubbery, the hedges, the trees — indeed, everything that could serve as a landmark — leaving in their place a barren and dusty field. It was as if a cyclone had blown through, sweeping away everything down to the bare ground.

Sally's eyes filled with tears as she looked around, bewildered. "We must have come to the wrong place, Mother," she cried. "This can't be our home."

"No, Sally, this is the place," her mother replied soberly, "but it isn't our home — nor can it ever be again."

Then, with Louise's help, she attempted to locate the line separating their land from the McNutt's. The railroad on one side and the public road on the other defined the remaining two sides of the triangular lot.

"Now, let's see if we can discover where the house stood," Martha went on, summoning her courage.

"I think I can show you," said Betsey, who had been looking around independently. She led the way to a pit in the ground walled with stone. "I'm sure this is it," she continued, pointing down into the cellar hole. "It's where we hid the day the soldiers fired on the house."

"You're right, Betsey, this is the spot," her mother agreed. "But they might at least have left our chimney as a landmark. Generally they did that much."

Betsey smiled scornfully. "The bricks are here in the earthworks," she said, pointing to a line of breastworks which passed by the site of the last house. The bricks were visible in them, together with numerous mussel shells, like the ones then in fashion to use for lining walks and flower beds.

When they had looked over the entire lot, noting the graves of a number of soldiers that only served to complete the picture of death and desolation, Martha turned to her friend.

"I could never live here again—never, never, never!" she declared, shaking her head sadly. "Not even if I had the money to build another house. The place is too full of painful associations."

"I don't wonder you feel that way," Louise sympathized.

"Now, I must look at the battlefield," Martha went on, steeling herself, "for the first time, and I hope the last. While we were refugees in Alabama I heard a few details of that terrific fight. My Osage hedge supposedly played a part."

"That, unfortunately, is true," Louise replied. "Would you like...I mean, would you care to go over into the field and see for yourself?"

Martha nodded. They crossed the public road and entered the battlefield, which stretched before them all the way to the Columbia Turnpike. The wide field, now covered by tall brown weeds, was featureless except for the deadly mark of war. At the far end of the field, a few widely-scattered markers indicated where the dead had been buried. Their number rapidly increased as one advanced.

At the opposite end nearest the town was a long line of breastworks, and directly in front of these one could see a length of thorny brush, now brown and withered. Here the grave markers were most numerous, showing where the firing had been hottest.

"This tells its own story," Louise commented sadly, looking

along the row of brush.

"And to think that I planted those deadly things with my own hands, all the way around that four-acre lot." Martha exclaimed.

"I suppose any good thing can be turned into an instrument of destruction if an enemy is behind it," Louise responded. "When our troops charged into that brush hidden by the weeds, it threw them into confusion and held them under enemy fire till they fell four and five deep. Look at the number of markers."

While Betsey silently gazed on the scene of the battle and listened to the conversation of her elders, Sally had been wandering about on her own, taking care not to step on the soldier's graves. Suddenly she ran to her mother and caught her by the hand, "Mother!" she cried, pointing across the field. "What are those men doing over there? They seem to be digging for something."

Looking in the direction the child indicated, Martha and her friend exchanged glances. Two men were carefully spading up the earth while a horse and wagon stood by. There was a long box on the ground. To the grownups their purpose was only too clear, and Betsey's expression showed that she also understood. After a pause, Martha bent over her younger daughter and said in a low voice, "I think they are trying to find a treasure they lost on the battlefield." But Sally was not entirely convinced.

That evening, after Martha and the children had returned from their sad outing, Moses had a conversation with his wife. "I had a long talk this morning with Nicholas Perkins," he told her. "He wishes—indeed he urges—us to come out to his house on Friday.

BEGINNING AGAIN

He hopes we will plan to stay with them until we get on our feet elsewhere. Nicholas thinks I could be arrested if seen about town. Several strange men from the North have been hanging around, probably for no good purpose, he says. So he urged me to keep out of sight for a while and not forget that I am an escaped prisoner who was once an officer in the Confederate service."

Moses paused to light his pipe, then continued: "Nicholas has three children in their teens—all but Maud—and is concerned about their education, since there are no schools here at present. Knowing that I am an experienced teacher, he is trying to persuade me to open one. His sister owns an estate called Mt. Pier, which is only about a mile from his place at Meeting of the Waters, and he feels it would make a great site for a school. He has a plan he wants to talk over with me, which is one of the reasons for wishing us to come out to his house. What do you think of the idea, Martha?"

"It sounds pretty good to me, certainly worth considering, anyhow. You are a very competent teacher and, with Mr. Perkins' backing, a school might be started—certainly one is needed.

"But there is another reason we should accept the Perkins' invitation. The Cloustons are hospitality itself, but Mrs. Clouston is a widow, after all, and her means are somewhat limited. I do feel we mustn't burden them for very long."

"Quite right, Martha," Moses responded. "There should be limits even to Southern hospitality. I have felt all along that four guests in a bunch was almost too much." He thought for a moment. "Then we will consider that matter settled. I will let Perkins know tomorrow. He said he would send his carriage in for you and the children, while I carry our trunks in the Chickering wagon."

The children were delighted when they heard the new plan, especially Betsey. "Oh, joy, joy!" she cried clapping her hands. "I shall see Maud again and have someone to play with who is just my age." And she clapped her hands again.

On Friday, the Royces left for the Perkins' home after a grateful and affectionate farewell to the Cloustons. To get there, they traveled five miles out from Franklin, through a stretch of bluegrass country. Despite the prolonged drought and battle-scarred fields, that country was still beautiful. The woodlands had a park-like loveliness, since they were free of underbrush.

"I do like this country so much better than Alabama," Betsey said approvingly as they drove along.

"So do I," Sally chimed in.

The Perkins estate lay at the confluence of the Harpeth and West Harpeth rivers and was appropriately named "Meeting of the Waters." The comfortable brick house stood in a wide lawn, with a flower garden to the rear. Beyond it were the various farm buildings and what had formerly been the slave quarters.

As they drew up in front of the house, Mr. Perkins came out to meet them. Mrs. Perkins came into the hall as they entered and welcomed them warmly. She led them to their room upstairs and made sure their small wants were supplied. She was a woman in early middle life, of very pleasing appearance. She had an air of kind and gentle dignity that won her many friends.

"Your children have certainly grown since I saw them last, Martha," she remarked as she smiled at Betsey and Sally. "Ours are so happy that you're going to be with us. They are planning all kinds of fun. Just now they are out riding, but they'll be back soon. Are you sure you have everything you need, Martha?"

BEGINNING AGAIN

ALL AT ONCE THE GIRLS, WHO HAD BEEN
LEANING OUT THE WINDOWS TO WATCH THE
DRIVEWAY, CALLED OUT, "HERE THEY COME!"

"Everything is just fine. Thank you so much," Martha replied. Hearing that, her hostess retired, saying that supper would be ready at six o'clock.

All at once, the girls, who had been leaning out the window to watch the driveway, called out, "Here they come!" They dashed downstairs to greet the Perkins children as they cantered up to the doorway. Quickly they dismounted, and while Edwin led the horses away the girls mingled in a joyous and noisy group.

At six o'clock, a bell rang and the Royces went down to the dining room. It was a surprise to see an Irish couple serving them. *Am I back in New England?* Moses thought to himself. *These are the first white servants I have ever seen in the South.* Instead of the usual candles, the table was lit by a tall glass lamp, which equaled more than half a dozen candles.

As the family members found a place around the table and each stood behind a chair, Betsey noticed that there was a small glass of wine at each place. This seemed to make it a special occasion.

"Before we sit down, I would like to ask Reverend Royce to return thanks for us," said Mr. Perkins.

Moses seemed pleased, and he hesitated a moment before speaking. "Before returning thanks I would like to say a few words, both to my family and to our hosts: My name, 'Moses,' has never meant more to me than during these last several years, when we have all experienced a terrible war. I and my family have literally been wandering in the wilderness. Through it all, I have felt that God was with us, most notably in the kindnesses shown to me after I escaped prison and to the family as we struggled back home. Now the Lord has led us back to our 'promised land' of Tennessee and Franklin. I thank God that I have the bravest little girls and the strongest, most courageous wife a man could ever hope for."

He paused a moment, then went on: "My mother used to say that life is but a series of new beginnings. Now, thanks to Mr. Perkins and his kind wife and family, we are about to open the door on another new beginning for us. So I would like to propose a toast to my family, to the Perkins, and to a new beginning."

"Hear! Hear!" was heard from all around the table as glasses were lifted and clinked together.

"Don't forget Frank and Patsy," Sally piped up. "They worked hard to bring us back here, even though they were tired and hungry and thirsty a lot."

BEGINNING AGAIN

"You are absolutely right, Sally," her mother agreed, "and even little Dolly, who was sometimes naughty, helped to share the load. We bless them all!"

Then Moses returned thanks and all sat down to what seemed to the Royces like a feast. It was a memorable homecoming and a celebration of the future rolled into one.

After supper, both families went out for a walk around the estate. It gave them time to think and talk about the exciting events of the day, and perhaps begin to talk of the future. Soon, the sun was setting and they headed back inside.

Betsey took her father's hand as they climbed the stairs to bed. "Mother and Sally have a story they want to finish before she comes to bed, so will you hear my prayers?" she asked.

"I will be only too happy to do so," said Moses, giving her hand a little squeeze. "I have missed that." It didn't take Betsey long to jump into bed and she made sure there was room for Moses to sit beside her.

"Is there anything you want to talk about before you say your prayers?" he asked kindly.

"Well, yes, I guess so," said Betsey. "Tonight at dinner, you said that Sally and I were brave, but honestly, there were a lot of times when we were really scared."

"Would you like to tell me about them, Betsey?"

"I guess the scariest was when we had to go in the cellar because of the Minie balls going through our house. And that night I helped Mother bring in a gun from the field outside. Then there were those people threatening us when we stopped at that big plantation on the way home, and the robbers who almost got me when I was riding Dolly. I guess that was all caused by the mysterious 'It' that I heard you and Mother talking about way back when the war started."

"Yes," Moses replied. "I didn't think the war would affect us. But your mother knew better, as she often does. Just remember, Betsey, there will always be mysterious 'Its' in your life, but none of them will be as difficult as what we have all just been through. You did what I asked you to do when I left: you helped your mother and looked after Sally, and I appreciate that more than I can tell you. Both of you had to grow up very fast. That is why I called you and Sally 'brave' this evening. And no matter what happens in the future, I want you to know how very much your mother and I love you both."

After prayers were said and the candle put out, Betsey snuggled down and thought some more about what her father had said. She was happy that the scary times were over and a new adventure would begin tomorrow. The Royces' oldest daughter drifted off to sleep with a smile on her face. She was going to love her new beginning!

✦ Epilogue ✦

THE ROYCES OPERATED THE SCHOOL AT MT. PIER until an academy was opened in Franklin.

Moses and Martha then rented a small farm for seventy-five dollars per year. This provided food and shelter. Martha and Sally loved the farm, while Moses and Betsey found that they were not born to be farmers.

In time, Moses was offered the position of rector at St. Timothy's Church in Nashville. He served his parishioners with loving devotion and dedication, making a special ministry with the less fortunate. During the cholera epidemic of 1873 he spent long hours tending the sick until he, too, succumbed to the disease.

After Moses' death, Martha went back to Walnut Hill in Greeneville, while Betsey and Sally relocated to Vermont to become acquainted with their father's family and to finish their education.

Sally was not interested in more than a basic education. She married and was widowed in a relatively short span of time. She and her mother moved to Hot Springs, North Carolina, and lived in a house of their own design. Sally rode horseback through remote mountain areas, photographing the life of the people living there, including their moonshine operations. She was dearly loved by the mountain people. Later, in 1906, she wrote and published a tiny book of 25 pages titled *Hot Springs Past and Present*.

Betsey was in the first class at Wellesley College and received a more complete education. She then taught school, married a widower with three children, and had three of her own. They lived at Harleigh, a large plantation house on the Eastern Shore of Maryland, thus fulfilling her silent wish as the family left the Polk mansion on the way back to Franklin so many years before (page 171).

The love of beautiful formal flower gardens, which was in evidence at Walnut Hill, seemed to be in the female family genes and was cherished by four generations of Royce descendants, including your editor.

❧ Acknowledgements ❧

A Genteel Spy might still be in a desk drawer were it not for invaluable help from so many special individuals and friends. I would like to personally thank the following for their support and suggestions:

Rick Warwick, director of the Williamson County, Tennessee, Historical Society, for his enthusiastic response to Betsey's manuscript and his urging me to publish this unique personal account of a Franklin, Tennessee, family's saga as refugees during the Civil War. Rick's vast knowledge of Civil War data, particularly as it pertains to Franklin and Williamson County, was priceless.

Scott Smith of Spring Hill, Tennessee, who opened his heart and home on my initial visit to Franklin, and his genuine regard for Moses Royce in the latter's ministerial service to St. Paul's church in Franklin.

Ruth Mitchell, a lovely hostess who welcomed me to her Franklin home and introduced me to many of her friends and acquaintances, who responded so positively to the initial draft of Betsey's story.

Donna Dupree, a professional editor, carefully edited the first three chapters, made valuable suggestions and encouraged me to continue.

Joe Cashia, whose warm welcome and tour of their beautifully restored historic home, known as "Meeting of the Waters," made me feel right at home in this place which had figured so prominently in helping the Royce's get reestablished after the War. He gave me free reign to do numerous sketches around the property.

To **Fran and Wes King**, present owners of Mt. Pier, the historic estate where Moses Royce established a boarding school after the War. The Kings gave me a most spontaneous reception.

Janice Keck, director of the Williamson County Public Library, gave me unwavering support as I developed the draft of *A Genteel Spy*, and also introduced me to the artistic community in Franklin.

Susie Sims Irwin, an established author in her own right, provided an excellent in-depth critique of my manuscript and insisted that Betsey's story should be published.

George Kegley, a writer and editor of publications for the Historical Society of Western Virginia in Roanoke, encouraged me to have the manuscript published "to share an account of civilian life during the Civil War, about which little is known."

Marie Gobel Levine, a visual artist and public school teacher, enthusiastically recommended *A Genteel Spy* as a valuable supplementary reading for classes studying the Civil War and made suggestions for a study guide.

ACKNOWLEDGEMENTS

Betsey Beach for her in-depth analysis of *A Genteel Spy*, setting forth a number of thought-provoking situations which made it suitable for adult studies.

Mike Lanza, a writer, for his time in giving an astute and honest critique, and to his eight-year-old son, Nate, who hid the draft from his parents so he could read it, too!

Margaret Critchlow, a great-granddaughter of Betsey Royce and an anthropology professor, whose appreciation of the editing process and of the maps and photographs reinforced my work.

Frank Kurtik, an author and historian, whose vote of confidence in *A Genteel Spy* by calling it "a page turner that definitely needs to be in print" boosted my spirits at a critical time.

Paula Hanback and her husband **James** at Two Peas publishing were always available to answer questions. They provided the final pre-printing editing, design and typesetting.

To **Richard Dougherty**, a posthumous recognition of his long association with the Greeneville, Tennessee, Historical Society and his excitement regarding Greeneville's part in the Royce saga. It was an ongoing hope and expectation of his that the book would be made available to the public.

A special thanks to **Dr. Crampton Helms** and his wife, **Ruth**, cherished friends from Morristown, Tennessee, who over the years have also urged me to publish grandmother Betsey's manuscript. I am indebted to Ruth and Crampton for their unflagging interest in my creative endeavors and for their warm hospitality through the years.

A GENTEEL SPY

Finally, and most of all, to my husband, **Herb Detweiler,** who went from a rather casual interest in my family background to giving enthusiastically of his time and energy to all the preparatory details of the draft manuscript—typing, researching, creating maps, and the appendix, graphic design and test marketing. The dedication Herb has given to *A Genteel Spy* is further demonstration of his devotion to me and his support for my artistic efforts.

I am truly blessed.

Gratefully acknowledged,

Judith Riker Damon

BETSEY ROYCE SPRING, CIRCA 1914
The brooch she is wearing
is now in the possession of her granddaughter,
Judith R. Damon.

FRANKLIN: Having escaped the Rebels at Spring Hill, Schofield's army reaches Franklin by noon of November 30. The supply wagons are moved across the Harpeth River (1), as the troops form behind breastworks south of town. Hood approaches two hours later and at 3 P.M. orders the attack (2). This onslaught sweeps the Federal advance back along the Columbia Pike, and the Rebels pour through the Union line near the Gin House (3). At the Carter House (4) General Emerson Opdycke rallies enough Northerners to plug the gap. Further attacks along the Federal line (5) prove fruitless, and the battle sputters out at 9 P.M. That night Schofield pulled his army out of Franklin and joined Thomas' force at Nashville on December 1.

FRANKLIN
November 30, 1864

❧ The Battle of Franklin ☙
Courtesy American Heritage

❧ Appendix ❧

(Items listed by page number)

Page 14: PICKETS   In a military sense, a picket was a guard posted on the perimeter of a military encampment or position. It could be a single soldier or a group of them spread out along a line. The purpose of the pickets was to challenge all who approached and to sound the alarm in the event of a surprise attack. It was a group of Confederate pickets who shot Confederate General Stonewall Jackson by mistake at the Battle of Chancellorsville while Jackson was doing some reconnaissance. He died eight days later.

Page 26: MINIE BALL   The "Minie ball" was not really a ball, but a soft-lead, conical-shaped bullet named for Claude Minié, a Frenchman and one of its co-developers in the 1840s. Minié also developed the Minié rifle, which was used by the French in the Crimean War, and Minié-type rifles were the common weapon on both sides in the American Civil War.

The Minie ball was designed to allow rapid muzzle-loading, which resulted in riflemen being able to fire several aimed shots per minute. Its large caliber (slightly over one-half inch, compared to about half that for modern army rifles), hollowed base, soft lead, and high muzzle-velocity made it extremely lethal, resulting in terrible wounds. Soldiers of the time boasted that at 1,200 yards (the length of twelve football fields, or more than two-thirds of a mile), the Minie ball could penetrate a soldier and his knapsack, and still kill anyone standing behind him. The soft-lead bullet had almost an explosive effect upon impact, easily shattering bones and blowing off arms and legs. If it struck the spinal column in the neck it could literally blow ones head off.

This type of ammunition, used by both sides in the Civil War, resulted in mass casualties that were unprecedented up to that time.

THE NEAR PRESS

Image courtesy of the Williamson County Historical Society

APPENDIX

Page 57: NEAR PRESS   This was a device for compressing cotton into bales. To the left is a photo of one. The long beams running from the roof to the ground were attached to the shaft of a large screw fastened to a flat plate which moved up and down inside a square enclosure the size of a cotton bale (about one yard square). The cotton was fed into the enclosure while the pressure plate was in a raised position. When the screw was turned by horses or mules harnessed to the long beams, the plate descended down on top of the cotton and compressed it into a bale. A bale weighed upwards of five hundred pounds.

Page 67: THE COFFEE URN When the war was over, the silver urn was discovered by some children who were playing among the bushes. It was in surprisingly good shape and was returned to the Broyles at Walnut Hill in Greeneville. When Mrs. Broyles died, the urn was given to Martha, and upon her death it passed to Betsey. She in turn passed it along to her daughter, Elizabeth. Elizabeth is the mother of Judith Riker Damon, the editor of this book, and in whose home the urn now resides. Note the slight dent in the rim. There was a small figure of a boy feeding grapes to a fox on top of the

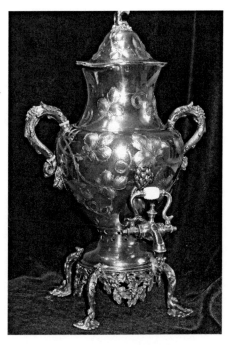

THE COFFEE URN
Image courtesy of the Editor

lid (there is a general grape motif to the piece). The fox was broken off in the accident. The maker of this piece was obviously a master silversmith. The detail is amazing!

Page 120: BREASTWORKS   A kind of defensive fortification. The term usually referred to earthworks piled up to breast height to provide protection to defenders firing over it from a standing position. Breastworks were often reinforced with timbers, rocks, logs, bricks, or any material which was available. They sometimes stretched for long distances.

Page 135: THE YANKEE CONNECTION   As mentioned in the Introduction, Moses Royce was born in Vermont. Moses had a sister, Jane. She married Edmond Morse and they lived in Rutland, Vermont. Morse volunteered for the Union Army and eventually found himself in New Orleans at the end of the war. When the war broke out, Moses, though born and bred a Yankee, followed his wife's loyalties and joined the cause of his "adopted country."

The matter of divided loyalty was not uncommon when the Civil War broke out. Feelings ran high on both sides, and circumstances sometimes resulted in brother fighting brother. General Robert E. Lee himself is a good example. A West Point graduate, he had a thirty-two-year distinguished service record in the U. S. Army. Early in 1861, President Lincoln offered him the command of all Union Forces. But Lee declined the honor, since his native Virginia was seceding. Even though he did not support the secession, Lee felt drawn to defend his native soil.

APPENDIX

Page 136: DARNING   Now virtually a lost art, darning was a common way of repairing holes in fabric, usually socks. A wood or ceramic "egg" was placed inside the sock, and the area with the hole was stretched over the egg. Then a network of interwoven stitches was formed across the gap, using heavy thread and a large darning needle.

In an earlier time, before television, almost every household had a small darning basket, in which was kept the egg and a variety of colored darning thread, along with the socks to be darned. A mother or grandmother (or daughter) would often sit with the darning basket in her lap and work on the socks while listening to the radio or conversing in the evening.

Page 137: SWORN IN   A little-noted aspect of the Civil War was that in seceding from the Union, the Confederate States were setting themselves up as an independent country. Therefore, when soldiers were sworn into the Confederate army they swore allegiance to that new country, thereby giving up their citizenship in the United States. In order to be accepted back into the Union as a full citizen, they had to renounce that earlier pledge to the Confederacy by swearing to "...defend the Constitution of the United States and...abide by and support all laws and proclamations which have been made during the existing rebellion with reference to the emancipation of slavery." It was that latter section which made this new swearing in particularly odious to many Southerners. In fact, a sizable number of "Johnny Rebs" refused to do so, opting to either live as aliens or move into the open country of the western territories.

Breinigsville, PA USA
27 February 2011
256446BV00002B/3/P